THE M & E HANDBOOK SERIES

Quantitative Geography

R. G. Woodcock

MA (Oxon)

Geography Department, Charterhouse School

and

M. J. Bailey

MA (Cantab)

Geography Department, Charterhouse School

MACDONALD AND EVANS

Macdonald and Evans Ltd.
Estover, Plymouth PL6 7PZ

First published 1978

7121 1703 2

Printed in Great Britain by
Hazell Watson & Viney Ltd,
Aylesbury, Bucks

Preface

Quantitative geography is often considered to be a "new" geography; it reflects a revolution in modern approaches to geographical studies. While the subject-matter of geography (people, places, landforms, etc.) has not itself changed, techniques today for handling it are certainly different from those of ten or twenty years ago. This is because a quantitative approach to geography, with its more precise and scientific techniques than previously, has been working its way through different levels of study. Initially practised at universities, some of the new techniques were introduced into "A"-Level work in the middle 1960s and have now permeated downwards to 11-year-old pupils.

Geography is so vast that only parts of the total subject can be considered in one slim volume such as this. However, examples of quantitative methods have been selected to show how different techniques can be used to analyse or solve geographical problems. After discussing the development of this new geography, the book outlines basic quantitative theories and methods; later chapters develop more detailed discussions of techniques, and apply them to specific aspects of geography. It should be noted, however, that a technique used here in the context of, say, population geography, could be equally well applied to an industrial or agricultural study—quantitative techniques have been developed to handle statistics from many different sources. Equally, the geographical location of the examples used throughout the book does not have any special significance—the techniques can be used on material collected from any area in the world. Here they merely serve to illustrate or support the particular technique or argument being discussed.

This Handbook aims primarily to cover the syllabus requirements of "A"-Level geography. Many of the techniques included will also be of use to first- and second-year university students, and by careful adaptation, the teacher will be able to use some of the simpler ones with pre-"O"-Level students.

Finally, a word of warning: techniques are only a means to an end, and not an end in themselves. It is vitally important that in all quantitative studies the techniques remain of lesser importance than the actual problem under consideration.

September, 1978   R.G.W.
                                                        M.J.B.

This book is to be returned on or before the last date stamped
below. Overdue charges will be incurred by the late return of
books.

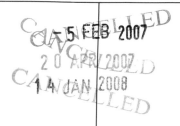

CANCELLED -5 FEB 2007		
CANCELLED 20 APR 2007		
CANCELLED 14 JAN 2008		

Contents

CHAPTER I

Introduction

DEVELOPMENT OF QUANTITATIVE GEOGRAPHY

1. History. When geography first appeared in the last century as a distinct study or science, it was purely descriptive: it set about to describe the various features of the world as it was then known. In its day, this approach to geographical studies was adequate, even perfect. When very little was known about the earth, it accumulated a tremendous amount of information and, in its detail and accuracy, much of nineteenth-century geographical writing is very impressive.

However, during the twentieth century the rapid growth in knowledge made a complete description of the earth increasingly lengthy, complex, and soon impossible. The growth of knowledge not only led to increases in geographical studies, but also to the development of subsidiary subjects such as geology, meteorology, climatology and later, biogeography and hydrology.

The subject became too large, too vague, too encyclopaedic. Geography was losing reputation and respectability as being too imprecise, and was even accused of collecting bits and pieces from many other subjects. In reality the reverse had been the case: other subjects were branching off from geography, which was the source or breeding ground of many subsequent scientific studies.

In the 1950s there was growing dissatisfaction with the status of geography in some universities and a minor revolution was initiated at Cambridge.

2. Modern trends. Cambridge University introduced models and mathematics into geographical studies, research and field-work, and they emphasised the need to quantify the factors under study. Thus was born what has been called new, modern, mathematical or quantitative geography. All these names are indicative of the changes that have been taking place, but not one of the names is really satisfactory. Geography is still geography, though much of the emphasis has changed from the days when a serious study of the whole world was possible. Now the aim of geographers is to seek general and broad understanding of the subject, and to support this by means of detailed studies of selected examples or samples. It is hoped that these studies will confirm the general ideas but also show how each example is unique.

In order to understand how each example is likely to behave, it is sometimes useful to formulate an idea or theory about how all examples of that particular feature should behave. This type of study sets out to simulate reality by the construction of a model (*see* 5 below). The words *simulation* and *model* have both become fashionable in geographical studies.

MODELS

3. Problems of scale. Geographical studies all have to face up to the problems imposed by scale, which in turn determines the amount of detail or knowledge required. For example, if studying soil types of the world, the British Isles would be a mere dot on the map and would be classified under the heading of "brown forest soils". This would constitute the kind of generalisation that is unavoidable in large-scale studies.

On a smaller scale, if Britain was the sole area under consideration, many soil variations could be shown. Much of lowland Britain would have brown forest soils, as these develop in areas of temperate climate with broad-leaved deciduous woodlands as the predominant vegetation. There are also podzol zones in the coniferous woodland areas and even peaty soils on some hills. River valleys often have alluvial soils and there are expanses of fen soil near the Wash and in Somerset.

In the case of large-scale studies of soil, climatic type is the main factor that determines the soil. On the smaller scale, the climate has imposed rather broad limits, but other factors such as aspect, slope, rock type and man will cause local variations.

When studying drainage patterns, again there will be great variations according to the scale. For example, the basin of the Mississippi-Missouri covers nearly half the U.S.A., and could only be studied on maps, as such a large area could not be investigated in the field. Compare this with a small drainage system that would develop on a pile of coal-mine debris, and a dendritic pattern might emerge, looking very much like a miniature Mississippi basin.

Herein lies one of the major aspects of the new approach to

geography. The generalisations and basic principle can be studied on a map (or in a book) indoors and this would be old-fashioned geography. In order to support or prove this theory, a detailed study of a sample, or an example, would follow, and this enables precision to be added to the original general descriptive comments. This constitutes new geography.

The generalisation provides the model or the theory, thereby acting as a framework into which more detailed studies should fit. Practical studies, including local field-work, should follow, to provide more precise information and knowledge.

Another example to show the significance of scale of studies would concern world climatic and vegetation types. On a world scale the tropical forests, savanna and Mediterranean lands are reasonable generalisations, but on close inspection no two areas are identical; therefore, one stretch of tropical forest is different from the next.

The study of macro-climates (that is, on a world or continental scale) is vague and easily criticised. This is why the idea of world climatic regions and vegetation types might be considered rather old-fashioned; yet it provides a model, or framework, into which all the local variations can be fitted.

The study of small or micro-climatic regions reveals that each area is unique. Therefore the possibility of studying every part of the world is as ridiculous as the idea that the whole world fits neatly into only eight or ten climatic types. The generalisations are unreliable but within the broad outline of a world classification, selected micro or sample studies can be achieved.

4. Field-work. There are few geographers who do not acknowledge the value of field-work at all scales of geographical study. The scope of field-work is vast, and rural or urban areas, whether local or distant, can be studied at many different scales, from a variety of viewpoints.

All too often the term "field-work" has been equated with "field-trip", relatively easily organised and descriptively useful in giving students first-hand knowledge of an area; the field-trip clearly has its uses but relying primarily on descriptive explanations is an inadequate substitute for real field-work, which involves the measurement and analysis of relevant aspects of information.

5. Models. A geographical model is an idealised representation of the real world, designed to demonstrate some or all of its properties as well as the behaviour of individuals living within it. Maps are simply scaled-down models of the universe and are known as *iconic* models. By displaying people as points on a map, the geographer employs an *analog* model. A third type of model is the *symbolic* model, which involves real-world phenomena represented as mathematical expressions. Isoline maps (*see* II, 7) showing densities may be called symbolic models. Finally, the most obvious model is the *hardware* or *physical* model, used in demonstrations or experiments. The globe and the wave-tank are two good examples.

Models do not hold all the answers to geographical problems, since there is no way that the multi-variable world can be scaled down without losing some accuracy and detail. Models do provide a basis for research, however, from which ideas can be developed. Simplification is their greatest danger, as they may make phenomena look deceptively straightforward.

Two very well-known geographical theorists, von Thünen (in 1826) and Christaller (in 1933) both used the sample-study idea by closely investigating geographical phenomena in their home areas; they indulged in local studies. They then extracted ideas or principles from their samples and tried to apply them to all other parts of the world. Both these geographers were ahead of their time as they used some quantification and then drew up theories to see how other areas would fit into the basic models. There were, and still are, surprising similarities between von Thünen's model (*see* IX, 7) and agricultural patterns in many parts of the world. The same is also true of Christaller's model (*see* VIII, 14–16).

These models are easily criticised because they are not perfect. However, instead of criticising the obvious weaknesses, it is more profitable to consider the accuracies and usefulness of these ideas. It is remarkable that these old models may still be relevant in the 1970s.

Variations from, and exceptions to, models can usually be accounted for by a detailed study of the local geography. Simple models can be related to a wide range of conditions and environments and they can also demonstrate possible future developments. This enables predictions to be made.

PROBLEM-SOLVING TECHNIQUE

6. Outline of the method. In setting out on a course of study for any geographical topic, a problem-solving technique is the best approach to follow. This type of approach involves the following steps:

(*a*) When the problem has been defined, it should be studied in the classroom and a hypothesis for solving or explaining the problem devised.

(*b*) Relevant information should then be collected from the field that can be used to test this hypothesis.

(*c*) The information collected should next be displayed in the most appropriate and useful form.

(*d*) This should then be analysed, and in the light of the results or conclusions, the hypothesis rejected or accepted.

This problem-solving technique can be displayed diagrammatically, as in Fig. 1.

7. Constructing the hypothesis. Geographers look for the causes behind relationships between phenomena: they must eliminate relationships occurring by chance. If the distribution of objects under study is the result of chance factors, there is little point in trying to explain the reasons for the distribution. Statistical techniques can be used to attempt to estimate the probability that sampled facts are the result of chance.

Before a statistical test is employed, a hypothesis (a theory to be proved or rejected) should be established in precise terms. The initial proposition or *null hypothesis* (H_0) states that two samples selected are from the same population (all the individuals in the study together, be they all the individual plants in a field of wheat or all the individual people in a country). It also states that there is a high probability that any observed differences between them are due to chance. H_1 is an alternative hypothesis, stating that the differences between two samples are so great that they are unlikely to have occurred by chance alone, and therefore the two samples must come from two different populations. They are not part of the same group.

If a small woodland appears to have slightly more of a species of butterfly than an agricultural area, the null hypothesis would state that there was no significant difference between the two amounts: the discrepancy was merely due to chance. H_1, how-

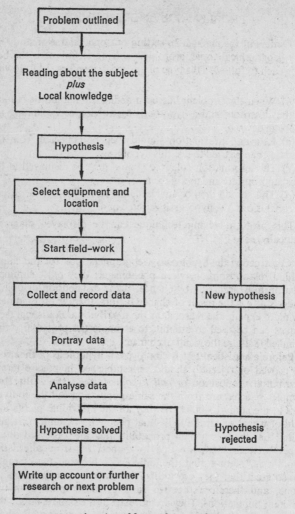

FIG. 1 *A problem-solving technique.*

ever, will state that the two sets of values are significantly different, and if our statistical test rejects H_0 and accepts H_1, then it

will be necessary to look for reasons for the difference in numbers to exist.

8. Collecting and portraying information.

Information may be obtained from a variety of sources, such as:

(a) *books*—textbooks, reference books, timetables, telephone directories, etc.;

(b) *maps*—O.S. maps, topological maps, dot maps, etc.;

(c) *questionnaires*—of your own devising or government census-returns, etc.;

(d) *field studies*—measurements, maps, sketches, etc., made from your own field-work.

The information that has been collected can be shown in a variety of ways. Increasingly popular is the use of maps, diagrams, charts and tables. The use of maps containing statistical information is particularly helpful. These maps are called *cartograms*. Cartograms cannot necessarily show all the relevant information but in order to be useful, they must show correct information and they must be clear and concise. No cartogram is perfect, as criticism is invariably possible. This is because of the difficulty of the task, which is to convert dreary written information into a form which is clear, diagrammatic, easy to construct and easy to interpret. Different cartograms will have differing degrees of success in achieving these aims.

9. Analysis of information.

The third stage of a geographical study is to analyse the available information to enable conclusions to be drawn and the hypothesis accepted or rejected. The question to answer or the problem to solve should be proved in the final analysis to the solution.

PROGRESS TEST 1

1. What is the difference between qualitative and quantitative geography? **(1, 2)**

2. Explain how geographical studies can be influenced by the problems of scale. **(3)**

3. Why do geographers construct models? What are their advantages in studying various phenomena? Name four different types of geographical model. **(5)**

4. What is meant by a problem-solving technique? What are the stages involved in such an approach to study? **(6–9)**

CHAPTER II

Map-work

INTRODUCTION

1. Ordnance Survey maps. The first official mapping of the United Kingdom began in 1745, with the Army. In 1765, General William Roy was appointed Surveyor-General and he pressed for a national survey. The base line was surveyed in 1783 and by 1853 the primary triangulation of the British Isles was completed. The Ordnance Survey was officially established in 1791 and the first one-inch map, of Kent, was published in 1801. Changes have appeared regularly since that time, up to and including the metrication of British maps, which started in 1974 with the appearance of the first 1:50,000 maps.

2. Map scales. The most popular map in the past has been the one-inch-to-one-mile map, with the representative fraction of 1:63,360. This representative fraction means that one unit (inch, foot, centimetre or metre) on the map represents 63,360 of the same units on the surface of the earth. These 1:63,360 maps have now been replaced by the metric 1:50,000 maps. There are still, however, special tourist edition maps of selected areas on the one-inch-to-one-mile scale. There are smaller-scale maps such as the quarter inch (1:250,000), which cover England, Wales and Scotland in seventeen sheets. There are 1:625,000 maps which cover this area in two sheets.

Larger-scale maps include the two-and-a-half-inch maps, which are really 1:25,000, not quite two-and-a-half inches to the mile. These cover England, Wales and Scotland excluding parts of the Highlands and Islands. There are six-inch maps, or 1:10,560, which are gradually being replaced by the 1:10,000. Sheets with a scale of 1:1250 (approximately fifty inches to the mile) cover the larger urban areas, and the 1:2500 (approximately twenty-five inches to the mile) cover most of lowland England, Wales and Scotland.

3. Map interpretation. Maps represent one of the geographer's most useful tools. An old definition of geography regarded the subject as a study of "maps and chaps". Map-reading will enable information to be extracted from, or read off, the map. Continued practice together with learning and understanding in all aspects of geography will enable map interpretation to take place. This is an advance from simple map-reading and it means that by looking at an O.S. map, in addition to seeing what is marked, such as towns, hills or rivers, the student is able to understand these features more fully than the more superficial information might suggest. The student is able to read between the lines, or interpret the geographical background of the information shown. Although this is often very difficult, the "A"-Level geographer should be able to explain the existence of steep slopes, broad river valleys, small towns or forests.

Occupations may be discovered from O.S. maps. Mines, quarries, factories and farms are frequently marked. Skilled and experienced map-reading may enable functions of towns to be discovered by careful study of building shapes and patterns, presence of factories, docks, power-lines, roads and railways. Agricultural practices may also be interpreted from map evidence. Knowledge of rock type may suggest fertile or infertile soil, whereas close proximity of farms will show small farms and hence intensive agriculture.

Certain historical information can be extracted from O.S. maps. A different type-face is used for Roman remains (A.D. 43–A.D. 420) to distinguish these from other ancient relics. By studying place names, early settlement patterns can be traced (see X, 19, 20). On large-scale maps, where shapes and outlines of buildings and roads can be seen clearly, some idea of the age of settlements can be obtained. For example, closely-packed, rectangular blocks of houses probably date from the nineteenth century, whereas ribbon settlements are a feature of the 1930s, and open-spaced, semi-circular roads are typical of the 1950s and '60s.

4. Other maps. In addition to the O.S. maps, which provide a great source of information, there are many other types of maps, such as those showing geology, land use, or historical information (e.g. Roman Britain, England during the Civil War, and so on).

There are maps with special properties drawn to show a particular set of information, without considering too much about the accuracy of other details. These may be *topological* maps, a famous example of which is the official map of the London

Underground system. Here straight lines are drawn to show the pattern of the routes, though locations of stations are not necessarily very accurate (*see* **8** below).

A topological map may be drawn to show the location of the counties of England to give a quick impression of exactly where the counties are located, and also their sizes (*see* Fig. 2). You will notice that accuracy in other details (e.g. shape) is lost.

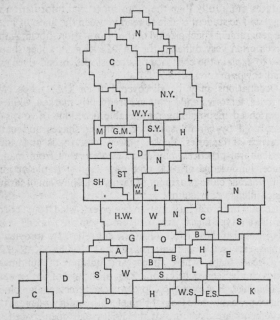

FIG. 2 *Topological map of the counties of England.*

Other maps include dot maps, choropleth and isoline maps, etc. All have their uses depending on the information it is required to show and the study being undertaken. A more detailed discussion of map types appears below (**7–12**).

DISPLAYING INFORMATION ON MAPS

5. Map-drawing. When preparing your own maps (or presenting any other information in diagrammatical form) it is essential to be neat. Neatness may take time, but it will ensure clarity and accuracy, which are what the study is trying to achieve. It is only by being precise that true relationships will be revealed; precision could also show up relationships that would otherwise go unnoticed.

6. Preparing your own maps. It is important to draw the basic framework with great accuracy. When this has been achieved, the next step is to select the material that is required and reject other information, which may be true and correct, but not relevant to the problem under consideration. By rejecting irrelevancies, the map will not become too cluttered.

By carefully studying O.S. and other maps, you will learn a great deal about how to prepare your own maps (although O.S. maps always show too much information in an attempt to satisfy too many customers):

(a) *Colour*. Study the way professionally-produced maps make the greatest use of colour. In the 1:50,000 series, the rank of roads is immediately perceivable: motorways, thick blue lines (blue is the colour now associated with motorways—as well as water! Road signs, for example, on and leading to motorways are blue); major trunk-roads, dark red; B-roads, orange; metalled but unclassified minor roads, yellow; minor, unclassified and unmetalled roads, no colour. The road pattern of an area can be deduced from a glance at one of these maps.

(b) *Scale*. Make sure the scale and size of your map is sufficient for the amount of detail you want to display. Cramming in detail will clutter and detract from a swift and accurate interpretation. Alternatively, if you make your map too large for the amount of detail to be shown, the spatial relationships will be lost.

(c) *Lettering*. Look carefully at professionally-produced maps. The choice of lettering and its size is not arbitrary. The smallest lettering is used for the smallest features and settlements. In rural areas (on 1:50,000 maps), the main or prime village of a parish (usually containing the parish church) is in Roman lettering while other villages—even if they are larger—are in italics of the same (or smaller) type of lettering, hence appearing less dominant. Towns are shown in capital letters and cities and major towns in large, heavy type.

Notice, too, how well-spaced lettering is used to label large areas. Do not try to space the lettering too much, or the word will be difficult to read. The very fact that the word's letters are spaced will suggest that the label covers a wide area.

Position your lettering carefully. In the planning stage of your map, allow for the words to be added at points where they will not obscure detail and yet be close enough to the features being labelled to avoid confusion.

(*d*) *Symbols and abbreviations*. Symbols should be devised to reflect as accurately as possible the feature being shown (*see* **11** below). However, too many symbols and the map will be difficult to read. Would an abbreviation be more appropriate? For example, Cu for "copper" or Fe for "iron" are immediately recognisable. PH for "public house", MS for "milestone" and P for "post office" are all self-evident. Symbols are best reserved to differentiate between different types of the same feature (for example, the three types of church identified on O.S. 1:50,000 maps).

7. Isopleth or isoline maps. Some geographical distributions may exist on a continuous three-dimensional surface (e.g. the slope and direction of mountain sides, sea bottoms, etc.). In such cases isopleth maps may be used to display the variables. These involve the construction of isolines (a common example being contour lines indicating height) joining together control or sample points with the same value of the variable in question. Not all isolines will coincide with the control points, and the skill in constructing such a map involves a sensible choice of intervals made with reference to the number of control points. Joining control points of equal value will eventually lead to a trend-surface map that will give a valuable representation of the aerial distribution of the variable (*see* Fig. 91, p. 149). Shading may be used finally to emphasise the trend, using dark colours for high values and light colours for low values.

8. Topological maps. The London Transport map of the London Underground system has already been mentioned (*see* **4** above). On it, the routes of the various lines are shown as simple, mainly straight lines, displaying clearly where the lines meet and interconnect at various stations. The lines on the map do not try to give an accurate impression of distance or even direction between each station. The emphasis is on displaying the stations and the interconnections. Topological maps, therefore, are ideal for displaying networks of routes that, if mapped according to exact distance and direction, would be confusingly complex.

Topology is sometimes called "rubber-sheet" geometry because everything is stretched out in an elastic fashion. It is a good method for showing networks as it preserves contiguity (nearness), though it is unsuitable for showing distance.

Topological maps of networks are drawn as graphs, with nodes and edges. Correct terminology is essential:

(a) A node is also called a vertex, junction or place.

(b) An edge is called a link, route or arc.

(c) A region may be called a face or an area.

(d) A branch is a single line from a node (*see* Fig. 3).

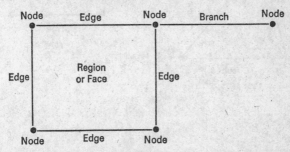

FIG. 3 *Topological map of a network.*

Mathematically it is not possible to have two edges linking the same two vertices, but in areas of inefficient communications these may occur. For example, on the railway lines of England before the Beeching-plan changes of 1963, there were two lines from London to Penzance and also two from London to Birmingham.

Graphs used to show topological maps may be:

(a) *A circuit*—without branches.

(b) *A tree*—these are directed graphs, with a flow movement in one direction.

(c) *A complex circuit*, e.g. a motorway junction (*see* Fig. 4).

9. Dot maps. Dot maps may be applied to distributions that involve *numbers* of items and require fairly detailed knowledge of the location of those items. They are better applied to small samples, the principle being to use one dot to represent a certain number of the items. For example, in a town, one furniture factory may be shown by one dot, or one hundred employees may be represented by one dot.

Care should be taken where the range of values is large to en-

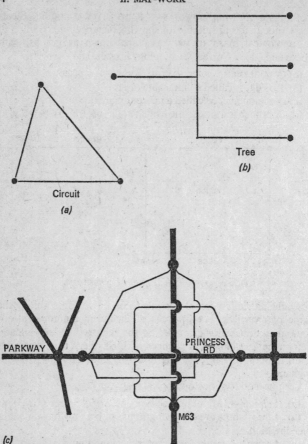

FIG. 4   *Types of network.*

(*a*) a circuit; (*b*) A tree; (*c*) a complex circuit. Strictly, all junctions are nodes, but in geography it is usual in transport networks to label nodes only where large or important settlements or other features occur.

sure that dots do not merge. Thus the size of dot and what it represents has to be carefully considered.

Where information is poor, dots may be distributed evenly over the area of study. Obviously where records are good a high

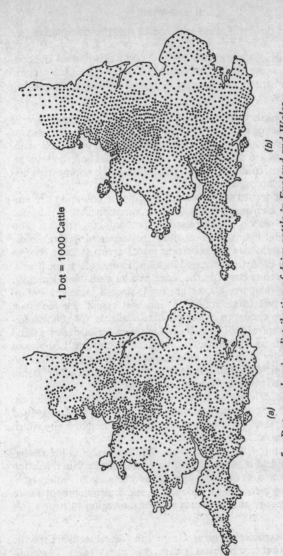

1 Dot = 1000 Cattle

(a)

(b)

FIG. 5   *Dot map showing distribution of dairy cattle in England and Wales.*

On map (a) the distribution is marked approximately where there is a high density of dairying. On map (b) the distribution is based on information gathered for each county, and the dots are placed evenly over each county. Map (a) is the more useful.

density of dots will stand out and be visually informative (*see* Fig. 5).

A lack of information can easily distort a distribution and convey totally the wrong impression. Even though they appear simple constructions, care and thought is necessary in preparing these maps.

10. Choropleth maps. Isopleth maps mentioned above (*see* 7) show points of equal value over an area joined together by isolines just as contours link places of equal height on an O.S. map. These maps are not reliant on area boundaries and show values in a smooth, continuous form rather than in the abrupt steps displayed by choropleth maps.

Straightforward techniques of shading or colouring are employed in choropleth maps to show variation between defined regions. Numbers are expressed in standardised form in a ratio to area, and figures such as totals are converted from absolute data into ratio data (areas become percentages and totals become densities). Each area bounded by a district boundary line is allocated to a class based on the range of data available. Generally, not more than five classes are used, since a large number of divisions will cause confusion and will complicate the map. Classes are chosen to reflect the data available. Cumulative frequency graphs (*see* IV, 2–7) display the range of data well and may be the basis on which to decide class intervals. Low values are generally expressed in light colours or shades which blend up the scale to dark textures for the higher values. White is not usually used because it suggests emptiness.

The choropleth map lacks the continuity of the isopleth map but is easy to construct and simple to interpret. The standardised value calculated for any one area suggests a homogeneity which does not reflect local variation.

The map in Fig. 6 shows unemployment figures in the Derbyshire Coalfield in choropleth form, adapted to explain migration within an area. A flow-line diagram may be a useful display technique using arrows to show direction, and drawn in proportion to the percentage of movements made from region to region (*see* XI, 16).

11. Geomorphological maps. Geomorphological maps are specific attempts to record physical features over a scaled area. Few additional details are used, usually just the relevant reference points to ensure proper orientation.

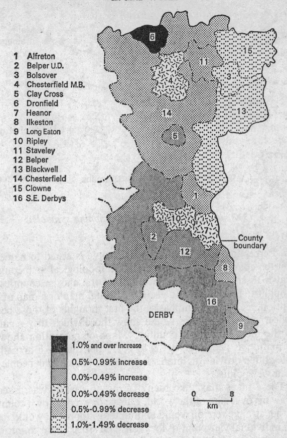

1 Alfreton
2 Belper U.D.
3 Bolsover
4 Chesterfield M.B.
5 Clay Cross
6 Dronfield
7 Heanor
8 Ilkeston
9 Long Eaton
10 Ripley
11 Staveley
12 Belper
13 Blackwell
14 Chesterfield
15 Clowne
16 S.E. Derbys

1.0% and over increase
0.5%-0.99% increase
0.0%-0.49% increase
0.0%-0.49% decrease
0.5%-0.99% decrease
1.0%-1.49% decrease

0   8
km

FIG. 6 *A choropleth map displaying population changes in the Derbyshire Coalfield related to unemployment figures.*

All maps have a set of symbols which represent features on the land surface. The geomorphological features are clear and try to retain the shape and scale of the real landscape (*see* Fig. 7).

As long as a key is used, these symbols can be altered to suit the individual. However, they should remain as uncomplicated as possible, to maintain simplicity and clarity on the resulting map (*see* Fig. 8).

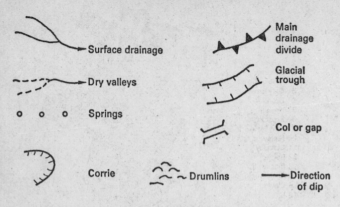

FIG. 7   *Geomorphological mapping symbols.*

12. Perception maps. If a group of people is asked to name the first ten counties that come to mind, a topological map could be drawn to show where the locations of the chosen counties are thought to lie. This would also be a mental map or a map of perception, as it would emphasise the first thoughts of those people concerned, and perhaps would show those which they regarded as the most important counties. Maps of perception show information as people believe it to be, rather than as it actually is. They often provide an interesting method of assessing people and their viewpoints.

These maps may take many forms. If anyone was asked to draw his own map of the world, Europe or even his own county, a rather strange version would undoubtedly appear. It would reflect an individual viewpoint of locations and sizes. Some countries or counties would certainly be placed inaccurately and some would be much too large or too small. For example, Norfolk and Devon are often thought to be small counties because they are not densely populated.

Maps of perception can also be drawn to show distance. By selecting certain well-known locations (e.g. Birmingham, Manchester, Bristol, Land's End, Newcastle), and by asking how far they are from London, it is possible to draw a map that gives a personal impression of locations. It will be surprisingly inaccurate. Figure 9 shows an example of this type of map.

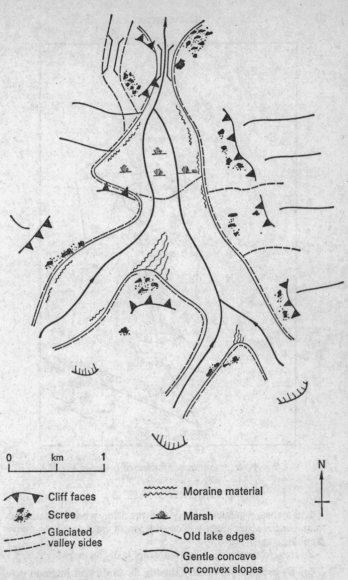

Cliff faces

Scree

Glaciated valley sides

Moraine material

Marsh

Old lake edges

Gentle concave or convex slopes

FIG. 8 *Geomorphological map of Borrowdale, Cumbria.*

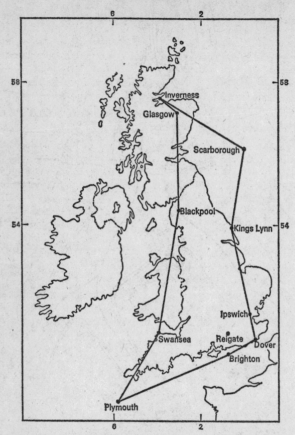

FIG. 9 *A perception map of selected towns in the U.K.*

PROGRESS TEST 2

1. To ensure greatest clarity and precision when preparing a
map, which factors must you consider most carefully at the map-
planning stage? **(5–6)**

2. How would you differentiate graphically on maps*!*

(*a*) by use of lines exactly tracing direction and interconnections, etc., (*i*) the main lines (*ii*) the branch lines and (*iii*) the

single-track lines, in a railway network covering a rural area of about 100 km² ? (8)

(b) by different types of lettering, the main centre, satellite towns and suburbs in a conurbation the size of Greater London? (6(c))

(c) by symbols and/or abbreviations, crops and animals grown in an agricultural area of 2 km² ? (6(d))

3. What type of map would be best to display (and indicate briefly how you would prepare them):

(a) the distribution of towns in the United Kingdom (without individual labels) containing main-line railway stations? (9)

(b) the bus routes in a small town-centre, to show as simply as possible the location of stops, and the buses' routes, numbers and final destinations? (8)

(c) the July rainfall distribution over a small island, showing areas of equal precipitation and the prevailing wind direction? (7)

(d) proportional increase and decrease of population in twenty clearly-defined parishes? (10)

(e) the landform features of a high limestone plateau? (11)

4. Ask five colleagues or neighbours to estimate the distance from your school or home-town to ten large cities in the country. Draw a map to show how they perceive the country and compare it with reality. (12)

CHAPTER III

Basic Selection and Measuring Techniques

SAMPLING

1. An abundance of information. In dealing with geographical information we are faced with a world full of potential data. It is impossible and impractical to look at everything, everywhere. We cannot investigate scientifically simply by collecting as much information as possible. It becomes necessary to select a limited amount of data, which might be regarded as representative of the "whole" or parent population (all the individuals, of whatever type, being studied).

In a land-use study covering the Home Counties, it would be an impossible task to cover every square kilometre. By taking a *sample* of areas it might well prove representative of the wider field and would certainly be more practical to study. Before a sample is made, however, it is necessary to ensure that the method of sampling is appropriate and that the sample is large enough to be regarded as a reliable picture of the parent population.

Finally, a study which includes time as a factor deserves special consideration, particularly if comparisons are to be made. One might choose to compare the situations now with the land-use of twenty years ago. Sampling from the past can be just as useful to the geographer in making comparisons, and the introduction of a historical dimension adds new and valuable information to the task of explaining the state of present-day land-use.

2. Random sampling. Each individual in the parent population should have an equal chance of being selected in the sampling procedure. If not, the sample will become biased and the results unfair. Random sampling discourages preferences and personal tastes possessed by the sampler. Random-number tables (*see* Appendix IV) or even numbers in a telephone directory will provide the location points from which each item is selected.

3. Point sampling. The area of study is treated as a map, a suitable grid being overlaid. The random numbers provide co-ordinates for each item. Point sampling is particularly useful in counts of individual species over any area, for example, in assessing the covering of spaghnum moss in highland areas in the Lake District. By selecting sample points one could produce a study without measuring every square metre in the region. Point samples are also applicable to data that has an uninterrupted or continuous distribution—for example, a study of an area's geology or land-use.

4. Area sampling. Once again using a map of the area under study, it is possible to select sample areas rather than specific points over which one's research might be carried out. By covering the region with grid squares, the random-number tables will provide the co-ordinates of the south-west corner of the selected sample square (*see* Fig. 10). The size of the sample squares will be determined by the size of the region and the object under study.

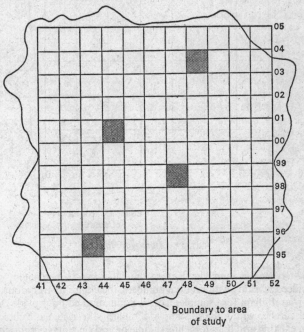

FIG. 10   *Area sampling.*

Squares that are too large or too small may not be representative. Areas may provide a representative picture of a region, but it is also possible to select a totally unique area giving the wrong impression entirely.

5. Line sampling. Another method of finding typical samples within an area is to use a line of study that, for practical purposes, will be no more than a few centimetres wide. The width of the line will be governed by the features under study. The ends of the line are selected by using random-number tables (*see* Fig. 11).

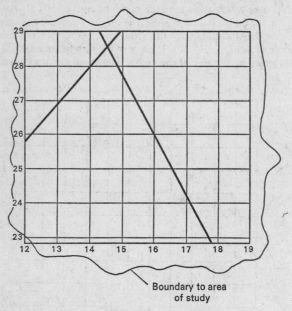

Boundary to area
of study

FIG. 11   *Line sampling.*

6. Systematic sampling. Rather than looking at every item or indeed working with random numbers, the choice of every fourth or tenth item, for example, from a population could provide the researcher with a useful sample. Similarly, the systematic choice of existing grid lines for a line sample or grid-line intersections for a point or area sample could be employed. It is obvious that without careful use this technique could prove inaccurate. In studying parasitic plants in a forest the systematic sample may coincide with a regularly-occurring feature, such as a footpath or clearing. Care must be taken in adapting the sample without being too biased.

7. Stratified sampling. Considerable information is necessary about the parent population to allow this type of sample to be taken with any reliability. With a detailed knowledge of various grass species in any area, each grass type should be included in the sample in proportion to its existence in the parent population before the study of insect habits could be continued. This method allows for sub-groups in the population and ensures a full coverage of the whole population.

8. Sample size. To be sure of measuring the parent population accurately it would be necessary to involve every individual. This is often impractical and consequently the sample used should be big enough to reflect the population parameters accurately but at the same time be small enough to be manageable. Opinion polls before elections are an example of samples that are generally too small to be reliable and consequently one should not place too much confidence on their findings. In 1966 a 10% census gave useful information concerning the United Kingdom's population. It is still necessary, however, to hold full censuses at ten-yearly intervals (e.g. 1961–1971) to provide truly accurate information on the population. There has been some concern over the cost of a full census and the value of such an expensive survey must be compared with the benefits gained from the results. It seems unlikely that the 1981 census will be affected by a lack of funds despite the cancellation of the 1976 10% survey.

SHAPES AND SIZES

9. Defining shapes and measuring their sizes. The shape and size of countries, mountains, etc., may help to determine economic and human developments. For example, a long, narrow country may have difficulties not to be encountered in a circular or square one. How can shape and size be defined and quantified, as merely to say long, narrow, square, circular, large, small is too imprecise for modern study?

Shape will show up clearly when mapped, but for comparison

of several areas definitions and measurements will be necessary. The measurement of longest axes, broad axes, greatest distance from central point, and maximum dimensions, may all be used to display shape.

(*a*) *Defining shape.* Long and broad axes may be drawn, the long axis extending from the two most distant points of the area. The broad axis will be at right angles to it, and will show the maximum breadth (*see* Fig. 12).

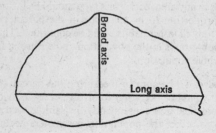

FIG. 12   *Defining an irregular area's shape.*

(*b*) *Measuring the size of shapes.*

(*i*) A method which uses graph-paper involves making a tracing of the outline of the area under consideration. The total number of squares can then be calculated easily to give an accurate answer.

(*ii*) If many unusual or irregular areas are to be measured for comparison, the use of standard shapes drawn in the centre of graph-paper may be helpful. Standard shapes may consist of a triangle, a square or any other measurable area.

First trace the area to be measured (area A—*see* Fig. 13(*a*)—) and superimpose triangle B on to it to give the best fit possible. Draw over the outermost line of A and B combined, and count the number of squares on the graph-paper within this perimeter. Next count the number of squares common to both A and B (shaded area in Fig. 13(*a*)). Divide the total number of squares that are common to both (*x*) by the total number of squares (*y*), and subtract the result from one in order to produce an index number. Use the formula:

$$1 - \frac{x}{y} = r \quad \text{where } r \text{ is the index number.}$$

Then superimpose the best fit square C on to A (*see* Fig. 13(*b*)), and work out the index number. Continue this process with the same area over as many shapes as are considered desirable. The lowest value of *r* would be the best answer.

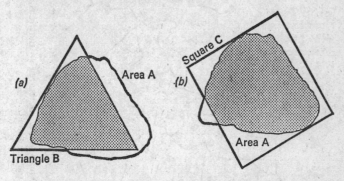

FIG. 13   *Comparing irregular shapes.*

(*a*) The shaded part is common to area A and triangle B; (*b*) the shaded part is common to area A and square C.

Repeat the procedure for the second, third and subsequent areas to be measured and work out their index numbers.

This technique is useful for determining the dominance of particular sizes of fields, farms or parishes in an area, but may also be used for comparison of urban areas or any other spatial phenomena.

Shapes may be cut out in cardboard to represent any of the areas mentioned above. By holding the pieces of cardboard vertically and suspending plumb-lines (first covered in chalk) from one apex and then from another, the centre of gravity may be discovered at the crossing points of these lines. This centre may then be compared to the location of the settlement, and the difference between the theory and reality may be explained.

10. Parishes. Parish shape and size will often reveal information about local historical geography as well as geology and soils. The importance of shape and size in geography are emphasised by studying parish patterns. The shapes and sizes may be the result of rock or soil variations, water-supply, communications, defence or a combination of factors. Figure 14 shows some parishes in Lincolnshire.

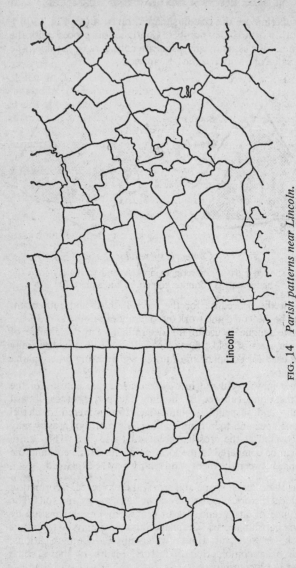

Lincoln

FIG. 14 *Parish patterns near Lincoln.*

If possible, this map should be compared to an O.S. 1:50,000 map of the same area so that reasons for the shapes and sizes of parishes may be found.

DISTRIBUTION

11. Nearest neighbour analysis. Nearest neighbour analysis is a technique adapted from botany, which measures the way in which individuals in a population are distributed over a given area. Botanists concern themselves with the distribution of plants, showing how competition within and between species affects the spacing and densities of plant types. Geographers apply this to people, factories, settlements and other items, helping to explain location decision-making and human behaviour.

This analysis compares the existing (observed) distribution with the ideal (expected) distribution that might occur under random conditions (normal conditions selected through a random sample). Human irrationality causes unusual decisions to be made, and it is the geographer's task to explain that behaviour.

12. Nearest neighbour analysis method. The analysis is as follows:

(*a*) Locate the points in the pattern on a map and mark them on a tracing overlay.

(*b*) Measure the straight-line distance between every point and its nearest neighbour. If the nearest neighbour to a peripheral location lies outside the area of study, it may be included, provided information is known about the point outside.

(*c*) Add the figures of all nearest neighbour measurements and calculate the mean value, which is known as the observed mean distance (d_o). The value may be compared to other areas of study.

(*d*) Calculate the density of points used in study:

$$\text{density } (p) = \frac{\text{number of points } (n)}{\text{Area of study } (a)}$$

(*e*) Calculate the expected mean distance between points, assuming they were randomly distributed over the area.

$$\text{Expected mean distance } (d_e) = \frac{1}{2\sqrt{p}}$$

(*f*) Calculate the nearest neighbour index (Rn) which simply compares the observed mean distance (d_o) with the expected mean distance (d_e).

$$\text{N.N.I. } (Rn) = \frac{d_o}{d_e}$$

$$Rn = 2d_o\sqrt{\frac{n}{A}}$$

If the value of Rn is near or equal to 1.00, the distribution may be considered (*i*) *Random*; (*ii*) if it is equal to 0.000, *clustered*; and (*iii*) if it is equal to 2.15, *regular* (*see* Fig. 15).

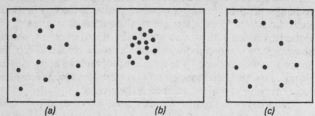

FIG. 15   *Nearest neighbour analysis.*

(*a*) Random ($Rn = 1.00$); (*b*) clustered ($Rn = 0.0$); (*c*) regular ($Rn = 2.15$).

This technique is similar to the chi-squared test (χ^2) which is mentioned in VI, **16**, but deals with individual point data rather than grouped data. Its strength is in making possible comparisons between regions. It is lengthy to apply and calculate, however.

Adaptions have been made to this method in that a linear approach has been devised. The relationship between shop types along a High Street or bus stops along a route can now be studied under an adapted nearest neighbour analysis.

Nearest neighbour analysis has clearly a part to play in spatial analysis. However, it has recently come under criticism and has been shown to have mathematical failings. Care, therefore, should be used when employing this technique.

PROGRESS TEST 3

1. Why is the technique of sampling useful and necessary?   **(1)**
2. Briefly describe the various sampling methods.   **(2–7)**
3. Choose a rural parish on a 1:50,000 map:

(*a*) Define its shape.

(*b*) Measure its size.

(*c*) Attempt, by referring to other features on the map, to explain its shape and size (compare it to neighbouring parishes if necessary).   **(9, 10)**

4. In a defined area on a 1:50,000 map, plot out the positions of individual towns. Applying nearest neighbour analysis, attempt to explain if their distribution is random, clustered or regular.   **(11)**

CHAPTER IV

Describing and Presenting Recorded Information

1. Introduction. Subjective or descriptive means of comparison allow too great a flexibility in any form of analysis and consequently there is a need to introduce statistical methods into research investigations. Having obtained reliable evidence concerning a particular field of study, comparisons with other fields and other experiments are possible.

CLASSES

2. Defining classes. In a field-study of slope angles in south-east England, fifty observations were made using a clinometer over a sample of slopes. Therefore, $n = 50$ (where n is the number of observations).

These observations were sorted according to their value into one of seven classes. The number of classes used can be decided in two ways:

(*a*) By applying the formula:

$$k = 1 + (3.3 \log n) \text{ where } k = \text{number of classes to nearest whole number}$$

The number of classes in our example is:

$$k = 1 + (3.3 \log 50)$$
$$= 1 + (3.3 \times 1.7)$$
$$= 7$$

This formula ensures that the number of classes best displays the range of data available. In Table I the data is displayed in ranges covering 2.5°.

$$(n = 50) \qquad \Sigma x = 1601.8°$$

$$\frac{\Sigma x}{50} = \quad 32.03°$$

Mean slope angle $(\bar{x}) = \quad 32.03°$

TABLE I: SLOPE ANGLES IN SOUTHERN ENGLAND

Class	Degrees	Slope angles ($x°$)	Frequency
1	23.0—25.5	24.2 25.2 25.4	3
2	25.6—28.1	25.7 25.9 26.3 26.7 28.0 27.5 27.6	7
3	28.2—30.7	28.3 29.4 29.8 30.6 30.3 28.4 29.6 29.9 30.4	9
4	30.8—33.3	30.9 30.9 31.0 31.4 31.5 32.4 33.2 31.2 31.6 31.7 32.6 33.1	12
5	33.4—35.9	33.6 33.9 34.2 35.8 35.0 33.8 33.7 34.4 35.9	9
6	36.0—38.5	36.4 37.5 36.8 38.0 37.5 38.1	6
7	38.6—41.1	38.6 39.0 40.6 38.3.	4

(*b*) By using the data itself to suggest class limits. Plot the information on to a cumulative frequency curve. The obvious

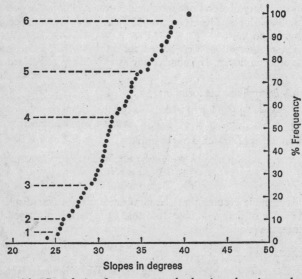

FIG. 16 *Cumulative frequency graph showing class intervals of slope angles in southern England.*

breaks in the distribution are found and will provide distinct points for class limits.

3. Display of data. The cumulative frequency curve can be used to display the information and classes graphically (*see* Fig. 16).

(*a*) Work out the cumulative frequency of each class:

Class	Frequency	Cumulative frequency
1	3	3
2	7	10
3	9	19
4	12	31
5	9	40
6	6	46
7	4	50
	—	
	50	

(*b*) Convert each cumulative frequency to a percentage of the total frequency (50) to give the cumulative percentage:

Cumulative frequency	%
3	6
10	20
19	38
31	62
40	80
46	92
50	100

(*c*) Prepare a graph, with % frequency on the *y*-axis and the degree of slope on the *x*-axis (frequency starting at zero, slope at the lowest class limit, i.e. 23.0°).

(*d*) Plot the cumulative frequencies on the graph at the *upper* class limits of each class.

4. Distribution curves. By joining the central points of each bar of a histogram that has been constructed from the data (*see* Fig. 17), a graph showing a curve is produced. When this curve is symmetrical in shape, rather like a bell-shape, it is described as a normal curve and the data is regarded as having a normal distribution. Data that is normally distributed is usually easy to deal

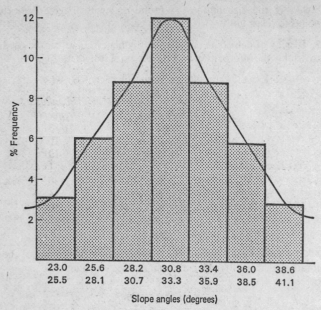

FIG. 17   *Distribution curve drawn on a histogram.*
Each bar represents a class of slope angles.

with and can be applied to a series of strong, reliable statistical tests, known as parametric tests (examples are used in later chapters). If the curve is not symmetrical, it is described as skewed and the data itself is less readily applicable to parametric statistics (*see* Fig. 18).

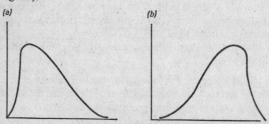

FIG. 18   *Skewed distribution.*
(*a*) Positive skew; (*b*) negative skew.

5. Central tendency. The set of data, or population, under study has three central values which are not always the same number. They are known as measures of central tendency.

(*a*) *The arithmetic mean.* This is more commonly known as the average and is calculated by adding all the values together and dividing by the number of observations:

$$\frac{\Sigma x}{n} = \frac{1601.8}{50} = 32.03°$$

Since all items in the population are included, the arithmetic mean will be affected by the extreme values and may not always be a good representation of the data.

(*b*) *The median.* This is the midpoint in the series, a number which has half the items below it and half above it. The items are arranged in series, in order of magnitude, and the middle number chosen. In the case of an even number of items, the mean of the middle two values is taken:

30, 31, 32, 33, 34, | 35, 36, 37, 38, 39
Median
34.5

(*c*) *The mode.* This is the most frequently occurring item in the series and this can be easily recognised from the histogram in Fig. 17 (i.e. 30.8–33.3). There may, however, be more than one modal class, which will lead to confusion.

These three measurements, or parameters, are useful in describing the central tendency of a population and can be used as comparisons with other populations. They may all be the same value, and in this case the population is distributed normally. The further apart they become the less symmetrical is the distribution.

This spreading of the distribution may be measured also, but by measures of dispersion. The range is the difference between the highest and lowest items in the population. A more accurate measure is standard deviation (*see* VI, **8–15**).

RELATIONSHIPS AND INTERACTIONS

6. Variables. Geography is concerned with an infinite number of features all of which cannot possibly be investigated, even with the aid of statistical techniques. Rather, the researcher looks to a smaller field, within the mass of information available to him, to explain the occurrences close to his study. He may look for re-lationships between one pattern and another, in which case he will continually encounter change with time on many scales. The variations experienced must be measured and as a result, the variables being changed, and the variables causing change, must be recorded, through field-work and other types of research. One variable, the independent variable, may be the cause of change. This influences other variables, the dependent variables. This relationship cannot be reversed. For example a gold rush will cause an increase in the working population but unfortunately, the reverse is not true.

On the graph (*see* Fig. 19) the independent variable is displayed on the "x"-axis, the dependent on the "y"-axis.

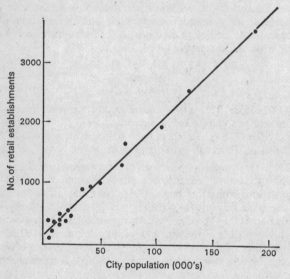

FIG. 19 *Correlation graph.*

The number of retail establishments (the dependent variable) is com-pared to city population (the independent variable).

7. Correlation. When data is paired, that is the variables have some association, it may be possible to show the association in a mathematical form. Some variables have a close relationship, some may have a concealed relationship and some, which should have an association, bear no relationship at all. Mathematical expressions can be employed to produce an index which measures how closely two or more variables are related. The index is known as the *correlation coefficient* and is based on a formula devised by a statistician called Pearson. This is discussed more fully in XII, 9–12.

GRAPHICAL DISPLAY OF INFORMATION

8. Scatter graphs. Scatter graphs can be used to show the relationship between two variables. Generally, a scatter graph should be designed with the knowledge that some logical correlation exists between the two variables. Where a causal factor, or independent variable can be clearly defined, it is scaled along the horizontal axis. The resultant factor, or dependent variable, is scaled along the vertical axis (*see* Fig. 20).

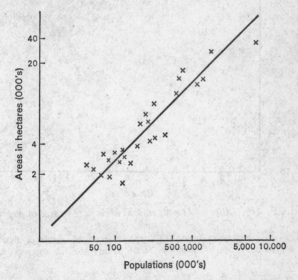

FIG. 20 *A scatter graph showing the relationship between the area of some English towns and their populations.*

Where one of the axes has a wide range of data, it is possible to convert that axis to a logarithmic scale. Special "log-normal" graph-paper is available. Both axes may be converted to log-log graph-paper if the range of data is confined mainly to one end of the scale with some very extreme figures not plottable on a normal scale (*see* Fig. 21).

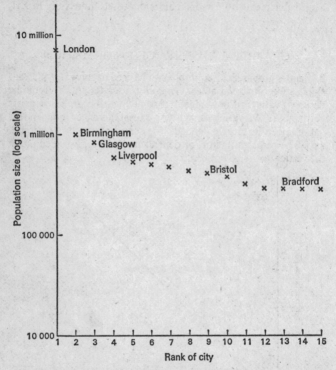

FIG. 21   *U.K. cities and towns ranked according to size of population.*

The *y*-axis has been drawn on a log scale as the range of figures is very wide. (Population figures relate to city and not metropolitan areas.)

9. Triangular graphs. When dealing with three variables, a triangular graph is a convenient way of representing the data in cartographic form. The triangle is equilateral and each side represents the total data from each variable. These graphs are more efficient if the variables are closely related (*see* Fig. 22).

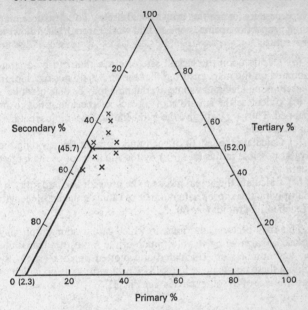

FIG. 22   *A triangular graph showing employment distribution in north-west England.*

Each axis of the graph shows a class of employment (primary, seconary and tertiary) and the percentage of the region's labour-force employed within that class.

10. Proportional circles. These are ideal for displaying information of two or more types on a map. The circles may vary in size, representing different quantities, and may also be divided in pie-graph form to show additional information. They are drawn to be proportional in area (A) to the quantities (Q) they represent.

$$A \propto Q$$

The area of a circle is equal to πr^2 where π is constant and $r =$ radius.

Therefore
$$\pi r^2 \propto Q$$
$$r^2 \propto Q$$
$$r \propto \sqrt{Q}$$

11. Procedure for drawing proportional circles. To construct a map using proportional circles one should work through the following procedure:

(*a*) Decide upon the largest size of circle that can be accommodated on the map, ensuring that the circles do not overlap. In densely-populated areas some overlapping may be unavoidable.

(*b*) Calculate the square root of each of the quantities to be mapped. Thus $\sqrt{Q}$ will give the number of units of radius required for each circle.

(*c*) Calculate the length of each unit of radius by dividing the largest possible radius (*see* (*a*)) by the square root of the largest quantity.

(*d*) Calculate the actual radius to be used for each quantity by multiplying the appropriate number of radius units by the length of each unit of radius (*see* (*c*)).

This may become laborious, in which case a nomograph may be used, which will give an estimate of the radius needed. Radii for key numbers are calculated and plotted on to a graph. By joining these points up, a line will give a useful scale on which to base the size of the other circles (*see* Fig. 23).

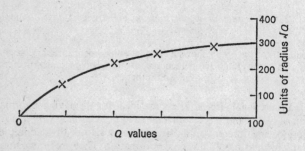

FIG. 23 *A nomograph for use when drawing proportional circles.*

Having calculated the size of various circles, they should then be plotted in the area or at the point of location on the map.

By colouring or dividing up the circle, additional data can be included (*see* Fig. 24).

Although this technique allows quick and easy analysis, it can be tedious and sometimes the end result will be crowded or diffi-

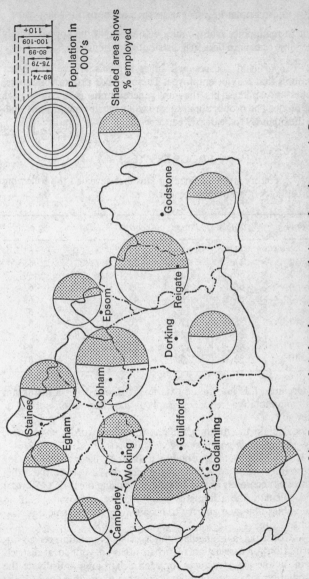

FIG. 24 *Proportional circles showing population and employment in Surrey.*

cult to read, since many circles will appear to be approximately the same size when data in a distribution is bunched.

12. Proportional squares and other symbols. There are other symbols that may be employed. These include proportional bars, cubes and spheres, but they are generally not as satisfactory as the circle. The proportional square will have its area proportional to the quantity to be displayed.

PROGRESS TEST 4

1. A county study of farming land has revealed the following percentages of arable land by parishes:

Parish	% arable	Parish	% arable	Parish	% arable
1	34	11	45	21	61
2	47	12	58	22	68
3	50	13	63	23	69
4	66	14	75	24	62
5	54	15	48	25	61
6	70	16	59	26	54
7	36	17	50	27	65
8	37	18	58	28	56
9	48	19	52	29	69
10	32	20	56	30	61

Organise this information into classes, construct a histogram and a cumulative frequency graph. Is the distribution normal or skewed? (2–4)

2. Explain the meanings of the following words: *correlation, log-normal graph-paper, normal distribution; variable.* (7, 8, 4, 6)

3. In a questionnaire, obtain the distance that students in your geography group travel to school each day. Measure these distances as accurately as possible (perhaps using the local O.S. map) and calculate the arithmetic mean, median and mode. Explain the values obtained and try to account for the extreme observations. (5)

4. Construct a triangular graph using population-census information for a selection of urban areas in your local district. Look at the age structures for each urban area and divide the population into young (under 25 years old), middle-aged (25–59

years old) and old-aged (60 years old and over). Put this information in percentage form for each urban area on the graph.   (9)

5. Using the information obtained for question 4, draw a map of your area under study and display the information in the form of divided proportional circles. Pay particular attention to the construction of the circles.   (10, 11)

CHAPTER V

Geomorphology

1. The beginnings of the new geography. The quantitative revolution in geography had its beginning in the field of physical geography with the work of the geomorphologist, Arthur Strahler. In a research paper on slope development published in 1950, Strahler applied statistical techniques in an attempt to relate form (i.e. slope angles) to the processes operating on the slope. This was a radical change from work of earlier geomorphologists such as W. M. Davis, who were concerned with explaining or merely describing a probable long-term history of landform. From Strahler's efforts geomorphology is now taking a functional approach, looking at landforms as a response to the processes acting upon them at the present time. Clearly this approach necessitates much more study and measurement of landforms (e.g. slopes) and processes (e.g. precipitation) in the field.

MAPS IN THE CLASSROOM

2. Interpreting maps. The landscape has been represented as a model in the form of a map for centuries. Maps have been designed to show places of settlement, mineral sites and a host of relevant details. Man has found a use for maps not only as a guide to discovery but also as a record.

The physical shape of the landscape is intricately displayed in the conventional Ordnance Survey maps, but great skill is needed by the geographer to interpret these abundant records. Recognising physical features is difficult, since one needs not only the map but other evidence such as rock type and past history, before definite conclusions can be drawn.

3. Relief and drainage. Relief is shown on O.S. maps by contours, together with spot heights, triangulation points and bench marks. The last three give precise heights at precise locations whereas contours are lines drawn through many places of equal height. They are as has already been noted (*see* II, **7**) a form of isoline similar to isotherms or isobars. Much interpolation is necessary in drawing maps, as not every spot on the map will have been surveyed (*see* Fig. 25). Aerial photographs have helped to overcome the lack of information. By studying the proximity of con-

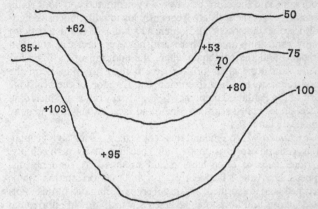

FIG. 25 *Interpolation of contour lines. Surveyed heights are marked with a* +.

tours, and the shapes they create, it is possible to decide where slopes are concave or convex, steep or gentle, and where dry valleys and other geomorphological phenomena occur.

To a geomorphologist, the word drainage will mean the river patterns. A map will show the density of drainage, the characteristics of the river and the presence or otherwise of drainage ditches, which are used to remove surplus water from areas with an excess. These must not be confused with irrigation, which means taking water to an area with a deficiency.

4. Rock type. The information provided by looking at relief and drainage will help to indicate the rock type occurring in any area. Some types are readily distinguishable, e.g. clay, chalk, whilst others are difficult to recognise, e.g. sandstone.

(*a*) *Clay.* This is soft and impervious and will invariably form low ground, which is flattish and contains many water channels, natural or man-made. Many farms may be marked, as clay often forms good soil. The length of drainage channels in a measured area is an interesting quantitative exercise.

(b) *Sandstone*. This rock may be very soft or sometimes incredibly hard. It may form low flat ground as in Cheshire or high rugged land as in the Pennines and Exmoor. Sometimes it is porous and may show a lack of surface water. It will often give poor soils and therefore be covered by heathland and poor scrub vegetation. As the soils are frequently low quality, intensive agriculture does not occur and unfenced roads are characteristic of many sandstone areas. There are, however, areas in southern England and the Midlands where the addition of fertiliser has made sandstone areas productive. In high ground, where the sandstones are resistant to erosion, e.g. Exmoor, or the Millstone Grit of the Pennines, there may be bare rocky outcrops, including steep slopes called scars or edges, and large expanses of marshy and peaty land.

(c) *Limestone*. In England this rock usually forms high ground. It is resistant to erosion partially because of its permeability. Surface water is often lacking and streams may suddenly disappear. Dry valleys frequently occur and their orientation can be mapped and quantified, to discover past climatic trends. Potholes, caves and limestone pavements, which are bare horizontal rocky outcrops, may all be present. Roads may be unfenced and farms are often widely spaced or isolated. These facts suggest poor pastoral farming, principally for sheep. Names of such features as "lime kiln" on maps may also give an indication of this rock type.

(d) *Chalk*. This is a pure form of limestone and will also contain dry valleys, but these will be more numerous than on the limestone. The slopes on chalk will be more gentle and rounded, and are often convex, whereas limestone slopes tend to be concave. The words "down" or "wold" will often occur, whereas limestone areas are frequently called "moors"; this word is also used in sandstone areas. Springs are common on the edges of chalk areas, at the junction of chalk and an impervious rock. The distribution of spring-line settlements makes a good human geography study, and can be investigated as a nearest-neighbour analysis.

(e) *Granite*. Most igneous and metamorphic rocks are hard and form high, steep or rugged ground. Granite is the best known of these rocks and occurs in south-west England, parts of the Lake District, isolated patches in the Midlands and widely in north-west Scotland and Aberdeenshire. Granite landscapes often show craggy outcrops and sometimes tors, which are upstanding lumps of bare rock. The vegetation is usually poor, peat bogs are common and valleys are often steep. There are few signs of settlement as the land is poor for farming. Old mines may be present as the igneous activity that formed the granite may also have created mineral veins.

5. Slopes and gradients. Slopes and gradients can be worked out from maps, though great precision cannot often be achieved because of the vertical interval which leaves 15 m between adjacent contours on 1:50,000 maps. If a hillside has a gradient of less than 40°, it would be regarded as a slope. Steeper than 40° is regarded as a cliff. A study of contours will show the slope, and the gradient can be measured by taking the vertical interval and dividing it by the horizontal distance between two points:

$$\frac{V I}{H D} = \text{angle of gradient}$$

If the distance is 2.3 km and the V I is 230 m, then

$$\frac{230}{2300} = \frac{1}{10}$$

This means a gradient of 1 in 10. A gradient of 1 in 1 = 45°; 1 in 2 = 26½°; 1 in 3 = 18½°; 1 in 4 = 14°, etc.

6. Average contours. Generalised contours may be utilised to show the extent of erosional surfaces. This will not always be very precise, but will give good general ideas. They are drawn by placing tracing paper over a map and making tangential marks on spurs that reach a certain height, say 90 m. These points should be joined up by a dotted or broken line (*see* Fig. 26), although a coloured line might be clearer. Similar, generalised contours can be drawn at 75, 60 and 45 m and other heights. It is not normally possible to draw continuous lines for long distances. Many hills,

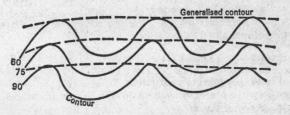

FIG. 26 *Generalised contours.*

such as the Chilterns, Downs, Welsh Mountains, will show remnants of erosional surfaces. These surfaces are remnants of former peneplains, which have been uplifted and eroded. Most of the level surface will have been destroyed by erosion, but fragments can often be discovered by the use of generalised contours.

Much can be learned from a consideration of geological structure, erosional process and stage of development. These three factors should also be relevant to map studies, especially when trying to explain and not merely describe landforms.

FIELD-SKETCHING

7. The value of sketches. This technique has lost some of its importance since photography has become so simple, yet it remains a valuable aid to field-studies and has certain advantages over photography.

Field-sketches need not be full of accurate, flowery detail, but should concentrate on the salient features in the landscape with the intention of reminding the researcher of the important geomorphological features that were encountered during the trip. Quick, bold sketches soon jog the memory omitting irrelevant details and clarifying the landform under study. Simplification is essential.

Sketching will also concentrate the researcher's mind on the landscape at hand, and may encourage more thought about its scale, shape and structure than would just a passing glance (*see* Fig. 27).

Whether the study is from an O.S. map, photograph or field-work, these sketches can be compiled. However, the best results are only obtained from a combination of all three sources.

Although sketches are designed to be employed quickly, under all conditions encountered in the field, the student must continue to pay attention to scale and relevant detail, as sloppy sketches with inaccurate lines may well mislead classroom analysis and destroy the point of the field-work.

8. Technique of field-sketching.

(*a*) Study the area in view carefully.

(*b*) Select an arc of view about 30–40°. Do not try to include too much on one sketch.

(*c*) Divide the view into obvious geomorphic units.

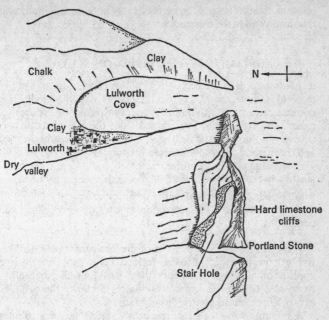

FIG. 27 *Field-sketch of Lulworth Cove, Dorset.*

(*d*) Draw in definite lines such as breaks of slope or the horizon, and work from the horizon towards your viewpoint.

(*e*) Estimate vertical and horizontal distances, using a known distance as a basis for your scale. Naturally, if a map is available, this is the ideal scale. Remember that features nearer to you will appear larger than features further away. To ensure the correct scale you may employ a useful technique which involves holding your pencil at arm's length horizontally in front of you and at right angles (or vertically) to the line of sight. Distances and angles can be measured off on the pencil and transferred to the sketch.

(*f*) Draw in prominent features, fixing these relative to the definite lines drawn earlier.

(*g*) Add details relevant to the study, e.g. villages along a spring-line.

(*h*) Annotate the sketch, using the margins and arrows, giving relevant detail. This may be marked in by note-form initially and then improved in the classroom.

DELIMITING THE FIELD OF STUDY

9. Measurement in the field. The problem of what to measure in the field is fundamental. There is little point in taking a multitude of measurements with the entire range of instruments, hoping that meaningful results can be obtained from the pile of data. It is necessary to go into the field with a hypothesis already planned and the method of sampling carefully considered (*see* III, 2–8).

Clearly the physical world is immensely complex and the problem of what to measure in the field means that we are trying to:

(*a*) isolate those parts of reality we are considering;

(*b*) see how those parts function or operate under simplified conditions.

10. Systems theory. Strahler, one of the fore-runners of quantitative geography (*see* **1** above), tackled these problems by the application of a "systems theory". It is useful for all geographers to be able to use this systems approach to clarify the complex network of relationships they want to study.

A system is simply a structured set of objects and/or attributes that have relationships with one another and operate together as a complete whole, e.g. the human body is a system consisting of cells that operate together as a complex whole.

Geographers in the broad sense are concerned with relationships between features of the earth's surface (*see* Fig. 28). The

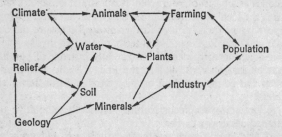

FIG. 28 *Systems diagram of the relationships between the earth's features that are of concern to the geomorphologist.*

network of systems of major concern to the geomorphologist is outlined in **11** below.

11. Types of geomorphological system. The geomorphological systems can be grouped into four types, each structured in a characteristic way.

(*a*) *Morphological systems.* These consist of networks of relationships between individual parts of the environment, such as that between a landform's geometry and its composition. Changes to one part (e.g. the composition of the rock exposed at a cliff) will cause a change in the others (e.g. the geometry of the slope of the cliff). Changes will depend on the number of components involved and the bonds between them (*see* Fig. 29).

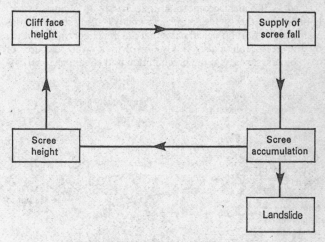

FIG. 29 *A simple morphological system.*

(*b*) *Cascading systems.* These systems describe the relationships between parts of the environment that involve energy or mass transfer. The output from a river becomes the input into a lake, and causes energy changes within the lake. It also carries mass into the lacustrine delta in the form of sediments.

(*c*) *Process-response systems.* These are simply a combination of morphological systems and cascading systems. The forms of land described by morphological systems are measured by their response to processes, described by cascading systems, with respect to time, e.g. the influence that a change in infiltration capacity has on valley-side slope and drainage density (*see* 12 below).

(*d*) *Control systems.* Control systems are influenced by man, e.g. dam-building in a drainage basin.

Having defined the network of relationships with which our field-work is concerned in all but the simplest cases, we have to decide which are the important relationships to measure. Some relationships will be much easier to measure than others. We will look at some of the problems and possible solutions within the framework of a process-response system associated with a drainage basin.

12. Definition of a drainage basin. This landform has been described as the ideal geomorphic unit. It has an almost distinct boundary in the divide, a specific area of study and contains many of the morphological parts that are under continuous study by the geomorphologist. It also involves a wide selection of cascading systems, e.g. the precipitation and stream channel cascade (*see* Fig. 30).

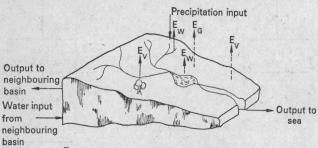

E_W - Evaporation output from water surfaces

E_G - Evaporation output from ground surfaces

E_V - Evapo-transpiration output from vegetation surfaces

FIG. 30 *A drainage basin.*

13. Black box. Let us assume that the relationship we want to study is that between precipitation and stream flow. By measuring the precipitation input over the drainage basin by a selection of rain gauges (*see* VII, 4–7) and the discharge, or output, from the basin, we ignore other relationships within the drainage basin system, e.g. evaporation. We are only concerned with the basic input and output from the system. This is known as the black-box approach because it ignores all other relationships within the system (*see* Fig. 31).

FIG. 31   *The black-box approach.*

14. Grey box and white box. Let us assume the relationship we want to study is that between precipitation, all possible storages in the drainage basin and stream flow.

The measurement of discharge compared to precipitation must now be explained in greater detail by considering a multitude of subsystems in the drainage basin, which may include vegetation, stream channels and the soil. There are energy and mass transfers within these and it would be a massive task to measure and analyse all the relevant cascading systems. This is the white-box-approach (as it looks at all relationships within the system) and would prove too costly and time consuming to be relevant to most studies (*see* Fig. 32).

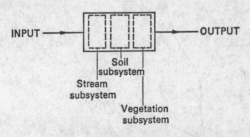

FIG. 32   *The white-box approach.*

The geomorphologist tends to work to a lower scale of study described as a grey-box approach, as this is concerned with cascading systems only directly relevant to his study.

THE DRAINAGE BASIN AND ITS SYSTEMS
—GENERAL DESCRIPTIONS

15. Classification of drainage basin: stream-ordering. The drainage basin can be classified according to the stages of development of the various drainage systems within the divide. This is decided by a technique called stream-ordering, which had its origins with the eminent geographer R. E. Horton in 1945, but it has since been adapted by Strahler. The finger-tip or outer-most channels are ranked as first-order streams and when two first-order tributaries join together a second-order channel is made. This classification continues until the main channel receives no equal-ranked tributary and flows out of the basin (*see* Fig. 33).

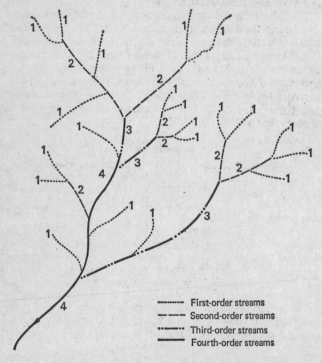

.... First-order streams
— — — Second-order streams
•••—••• Third-order streams
———— Fourth-order streams

FIG. 33   *Strahler's stream-ordering.*

The basin in Fig. 33 is fourth-order. Although this method violates its own distributive law, in that the entry of a lower-order channel does not always cause an increase in the order of the main stream, it is more widely used than another, perhaps more logical, model devised by Shreve. Shreve divided the network into links, the magnitude of each link reflecting the number of first-order streams feeding it (*see* Fig. 34).

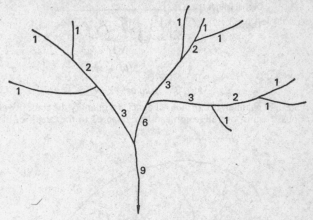

FIG. 34   *Shreve's stream-ordering.*

16. Classification according to drainage density.
Stream-ordering gives a clue to the stage of development a basin has reached and hence it can classify it. There are, however, other descriptive and quantitative measures that will classify drainage basins, drainage density being commonly used.

Drainage density is the ratio between channel length and basin area. A problem arises, however, in the definition of a channel. Does one measure the permanent channel or include temporary channels also? This kind of situation is quite common in geomorphological studies and needs to be considered seriously before field-work is carried out. Small-scale studies or pilot studies will often help clarify these points. Sandstones on Exmoor have values between 3 and 4, whilst semi-arid slopes in Dakota, U.S.A. have values ranging from 2 to 400.

17. Sinuosity.
Sinuosity of a stream is calculated by comparing the overall channel length to the length of the thalweg (a thalweg

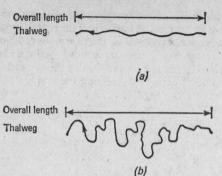

FIG. 35   *Sinuosity.*

(*a*) Straight channel; (*b*) tortuous channel. To quantify the sinuosity of various streams, overall length can be compared to the length of the thalweg.

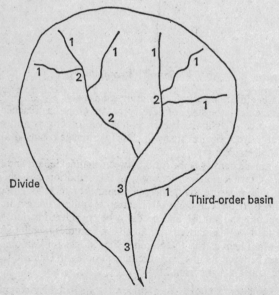

FIG. 36   *Bifurcation ratio.*

is the line joining the lowest points of a valley from the river source to its mouth and hence will trace the approximate course of the stream—*see* Fig. 35).

18. Bifurcation ratio. Comparing the total number of first-order streams in a system to the total numbers of second-order streams will give the bifurcation ratio. In Fig. 36, a total number of 7 first-order streams enter a total of 2 second-order streams and hence the ratio is 3.5. Similarly, 2 second-order streams enter one third-order stream, so the ratio here is 2 (mathematically, it cannot be less than 2). An efficient drainage system will have a ratio between 3 and 5.

19. Conclusions. These measurements provide quantitative descriptions of the physical landform of the drainage basin and its systems, and also force the geomorphologist to look for explanations to the values achieved. They may also act as indices which can be compared to other indices calculated in separate drainage-basin studies.

A SAMPLE FIELD-STUDY OF THE DRAINAGE BASIN

20. Problems to bear in mind. One of the major problems encountered by field-workers is the lack of time available to study physical processes. Slope movements or bank erosion by rivers are some of the more rapid processes in the earth's system but even these need years of study, unless there has been some particularly violent energy at work, e.g. a flood or storm.

It is not easy therefore to complete studies; indeed changes are so minute that measurements may be meaningless, especially if there are inaccuracies in the recording instruments or the recorder.

Some processes are simulated in hardware models and although these provide valuable results, it is not safe to rely entirely on these artificial conditions. Speeding up reactions may induce unnatural results.

Another problem is that of anomalies, which are always likely to occur, encouraged by man or unusual weather conditions. Droughts in Britain have interfered with water tables and subsidence has occurred in clay areas. Excessive water falling on drought-hardened ground will cause sheet run off and rather rapid soil erosion as dying vegetation cannot root the soil particles together.

It is necessary to bear these types of problem in mind and try to account for them in your field-work. For example, measuring a local river under drought, normal and flood conditions will give a full range of recordings and not just a biased sample.

21. Initial classroom mapwork. In the classroom it is possible to describe the drainage basin under study in terms of its shape and size.

(*a*) Delimit the drainage basin by tracing back from the main channel until the small tributary streams are at their source. Do not consider this to be the divide, however, since underground flow will contribute to channels and is therefore part of the drainage system. Take as the divide the highest point around the basin.

(*b*) Measure the perimeter with a chart wheel, being careful to observe the scale of the map, and convert the measurements to real ground measures accordingly.

(*c*) Measure channel slope by calculating how far the stream drops in height (use contours and spot-heights).

(*d*) Calculate the relief ratio, which is height above base level (the lowest level to which the stream has worn down its bed), compared to the maximum length of the drainage basin (*see* Fig. 37).

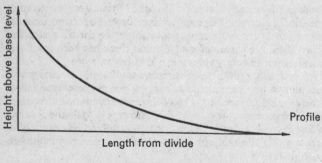

FIG. 37   *Relief ratio.*

22. Plan out the study. Before embarking on the field-work, it is essential to plan out exactly what you intend to measure and what you hope to prove or learn. In the following field-study, the objective was to measure the velocity of a river at various points along its course, and then to calculate where its flow is fastest.

(a) *Considerations.*

(i) Select a variety of sites giving the fullest coverage of the river's system. Here sampling techniques can be employed (*see* III, 2–8).

(ii) If possible, try to take readings at various times through the year.

(iii) Ensure a full understanding of any local anomalies that might cause unusual readings, e.g. an industrial plant employing the river water or an obstruction.

(iv) Measure velocities at various depths.

(b) *Equipment.* The following equipment will be needed:

(i) Small water raft or canoe.

(ii) Stop watch.

(iii) Telescopic rod or plumb line.

(iv) Tape-measure.

(v) Polystyrene balls.

(vi) Coloured, hollow, plastic sphere with adjustable weightings.

(vii) Ranging-poles.

23. Method. The following series of measurements should be taken at each site chosen:

(a) Measure the width and depth of the river so as to produce a river cross-section. In the field it is an easy task to measure a channel cross-section as long as one is prepared to venture into the stream. Fix a ranging-pole at each side of the channel where the water meets the bank. Stretch a tape between them and measure the width. Then place more poles or use a stiff metal tape at equal intervals across the channel. Make a series of depth measurements. From this data a cross-section can easily be constructed. The area of the cross-section will provide the basis from which discharge values can be obtained.

(b) Use the polystyrene balls to see if there are any unusual eddy currents over the stretch of water, which may affect readings. Bear in mind that wind speed may affect surface flow.

(c) Measure the distance above and below the site over which the plastic sphere will float to assess the river's velocity (a total distance of, say, 100 m). Time the flow of the sphere over the surface course and take more than one measurement to ensure a good average result.

(d) By adjusting the weight of the sphere, measure the velocity just below the surface and towards the centre of the river, to assess maximum velocity. Repeat the procedure at about 0.6 depth, again towards the centre of the river, to assess mean velocity (*see* Fig. 38).

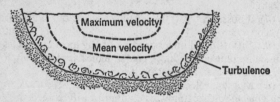

FIG. 38 *Cross-section of a river showing its different velocities.*
Measurements should be made at various points and depths to assess overall velocity accurately.

(e) Draw up a table (*see* Table II) on which results are recorded.

TABLE II: RESULTS FOR STREAM *x*

Point one	Readings m/s					Average (mean)	Anomalies
Surface	1.2	1.3	1.3	1.2	1.1	1.25	Calm conditions
Maximum	1.6	1.4	1.5	1.6	1.4	1.5	
Mean	1.2	1.1	1.2	1.3	1.2	1.2	Wide floodplain
Point two							
Surface	1.3	1.6	1.4	1.3	1.4	1.4	Higher reading caused by strong wind gust
Maximum	1.6	1.7	1.6	1.5	1.5	1.58	Straighter reach
Mean	1.1	1.2	1.1	1.2	1.2	1.16	of river

24. Calculations and conclusions.

(a) Mean velocity of stream at point one = 1.2 m/s
(b) Cross-sectional area of stream at point one = 100 m²
(c) Volume of water discharge at point one in one second is the cross-sectional area × velocity = 120 m³/s

Carry this out for all points of measurement down the river. Given the velocities and discharge figures, explain their values in terms of condition of the river, local anomalies, and the time of the year.

Assess, as far as you can, where the river is flowing at its fastest.

PROGRESS TEST 5

1. What geomorphological features can be identified on a 1:50,000 O.S. map? (2–6)

2. Prepare a field-sketch of a well-defined landform in your area. Relate this to an O.S. map if possible. (7–8)

3. Show how a drainage basin can be assessed as a system. (12–14)

4. What methods might be used to classify a drainage system? (15–19)

5. Describe an experiment that would show the various directions of flow in a stream. (23)

CHAPTER VI

Biogeography

AN ECOSYSTEMS APPROACH

1. Development. Biogeography forms an important link between the disciplines of geography and ecology, the ecosystem providing the fundamental integrating concept for the scientific study of many aspects of the man-environment complex.

Thus the spatial relationships geographers study are also the concern of ecologists, who study the distribution of plants and animal communities on the surface of the earth on both a macro- and micro-scale. The techniques developed by the ecologists to analyse spatial relationships, dispersion and other behavioural patterns have an obvious application in the geographical field.

Geography can also benefit from the application of techniques developed to quantify and predict the distribution and changes in plant and animal populations over time, to throw light on the behaviour of human populations.

2. The ecosystem. The ecosystem is a shortened form of the phrase "ecological system". The word was first used by Haekel in 1868 in his botanical studies (*oikos*—house or place to live in). The ecosystem is concerned with air, organisms and the abiotic (non-living) elements surrounding them: material cycles (e.g. the carbon cycle) and energy flows (e.g. solar energy inputs) that provide and maintain life in a balanced form. The study of biogeography needs to understand all ecosystem components, not just the trees in a forest but all the biotic (living) and abiotic (non-living) factors that make up the environment (*see* Fig. 39).

3. Equilibrium. Ecosystems are rarely clearly defined as the boundaries are transitional. These boundary zones are termed ecotones.

The development of an ecosystem (regardless of the scale of study) is through a succession of stages towards a steady state or climax situation from which fluctuation might occur from season to season, but to which state the ecosystem will tend under

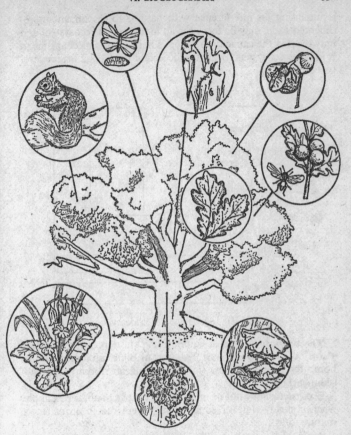

FIG. 39 *Some components in the ecosystem of an individual oak tree.*

natural conditions to return. To achieve this state, the multitude of parts in the system interact and will naturally, by a series of checks and balances (homeostatic mechanisms), reach equilibrium. For example, in ecosystem "Earth" the carbon dioxide content in the air gradually reached a constant level suitable to support life. The ecosystem components have since responded to maintain this balance, but man's recent massive fuel-burning, representing an interference with natural forces on an unprecedented scale, may be too large an input into the ecosystem and may overtax the capacity of nature's homeostatic mechanisms to bring the ecosystem back to the established equilibrium level (*see* Fig 40).

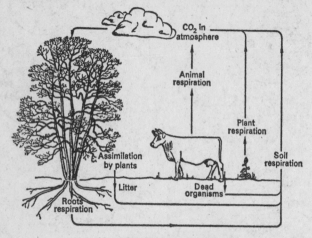

FIG. 40 *The carbon dioxide cycle.*

Succession to a state of equilibrium can be very rapid (spring growth of vegetation), slow (recovery of Bikini atoll after atomic bomb tests) or very slow (infilling of glacial ribbon lakes with sediment).

Ecosystems may not be in a state of change at all, for example, when a steady state or equilibrium is achieved in an ocean or mature forest.

4. Growth. Figure 41 shows a balanced system where small fluctuations might occur, for example during seasonal changes, but these are usually compensated for in the system, and recovery is quite rapid.

Some ecosystems may be in a state of definite growth as is shown by newly-planted crops. They absorb more energy than they release (inputs are greater than outputs), the energy being utilised for growth and stored in the plant as new tissue.

Negative growth is possible where the ecosystem is declining or ageing, for example, the limited life of bacteria on decaying

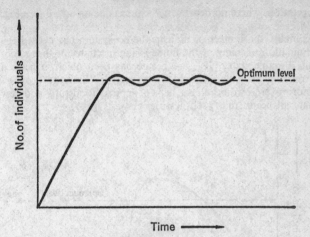

FIG. 41 *A balanced system of growth.*

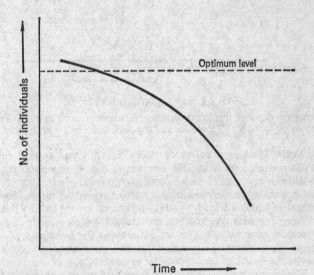

FIG. 42 *A negative or ageing system.*

vegetation, where no new energy source is being added (*see* Fig. 42).

Finally, the impact of man in the ecosystem has caused the elimination of many of the homeostatic mechanisms that maintain a stable state. His growth rate has been quick in general terms and now there should be a case for "limits to growth" before overcrowding and a lack of inputs (foodstuffs and raw materials) cause man's self-destruction (*see* Fig. 43).

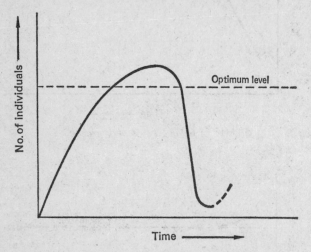

FIG. 43 *A rapid negative-growth curve.*

After the rapid decline in population, the curve moves up again as the surviving individuals reproduce and the population builds once more.

5. Scale. The biosphere (or ecosystem "Earth") is an example of a macro-scale system and the diagram in Fig. 44 represents the worldwide environment in which all life is present.

On a smaller scale, the biome is a major region within the biosphere in which distinctive plants and animal groups usually live in harmony with one another and are well adapted to the surrounding environment. One might consider the savanna grasslands as an example, in which distinctive environmental factors produce a wealth of species peculiar to that biome.

The biome is made up of many integrated micro-scale systems and it is this scale of ecosystem with which we are usually con-

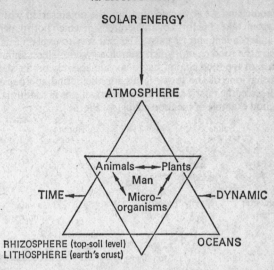

FIG. 44 *The biosphere.*

cerned when carrying out geographical field-work. The development of tundra soils may serve as an example of the process of succession in one mass system that is influenced by particular environmental factors. Eyre sums up these factors in a flow diagram (*see* Fig. 45).

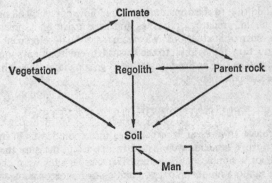

FIG. 45 *A biome (the formation of tundra soils).*

6. Food chain. At any scale of study, the organisation within an ecosystem takes the form of an hierarchy in which both dependent and independent species exist. The best way to explain this is to employ the food chain, which is itself a system. Here, animals at the top of the food chain (macro-consumers) rely on the successful behaviour of the lower levels for their food sources. On a small scale, the relationships between organisms in a stony stream is a good example of the food chain (*see* Fig. 46).

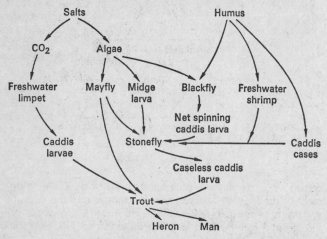

FIG. 46   *The food chain of a stony stream.*

In addition to the apparently ordered flow of energy along the food chain, predators, parasites and pests exist, and sometimes cause harm or fluctuations away from a natural development. The introduction of the rabbit to the Australian environment soon had disastrous results as the devastation of grazing land caused havoc to the sheep farmlands.

FIELD-STUDY OF THE ECOSYSTEM

7. Project. In a research project measuring soil depths in south-west Surrey, students were asked to select and measure the soil depth of a sample of fifty sites. The sample sites were chosen using random numbers to give point co-ordinates on a map overlay grid (*see* III, 2–8). This random sample was judged sufficiently large to give an accurate picture of the difference in soil depths in the area, although the technique may, entirely by chance, give a biased result by locating a disproportionately large number of sites in one particular area, for example, sampling with a bias to the chalk areas on the Hog's Back. A random sample, however, should result in the mean depth ($\bar{x}$) lying between the extremes of chalk and Wealden clays ($\bar{x} = 466.7$ mm, *see* IV, 5: calculation $\Sigma x/n$). If any sample is to be considered truly representative of the parent population the sample mean ($\bar{x}$) should lie close to the parent (or population) mean ($\bar{X}$). By plotting the sample means of several samples from our population on a frequency distribution graph (*see* Fig. 17 at IV, 4) the sampling distribution will show a curve approximating to a normal curve with the same mean as the parent population.

8. Measurement and errors. Measurement, inevitably, involves errors, whether caused by the instrument or by the individual. Errors have a particular distribution, just as any parameter, being spread equally about the true value. Most values cluster about the mean and describe a symmetrical bell-shaped curve. The likelihood of a value appearing near the mean is high and inaccurate estimates are more improbable than accurate ones. The curve suggests a probability that certain events will occur and is therefore called the normal probability curve.

The area under the curve approximates closely to 1.00 and the curve extends infinitely in both directions, 99 % of the curve being found within ± 3 standard deviations (σ) of the mean ($\bar{x}$)—*see* Fig. 47.

9. Probability. These values prove useful in geographical research since it becomes necessary to prove the statistical significance of a conclusion and the probability that a hypothesis is correct.

When flipping a coin the probability of displaying "heads" is $\frac{1}{2}$ or 0.5. Throwing a six with a dice has a probability of $\frac{1}{6}$ or approximately 0.17. From our soil data the probability of finding a depth of under 100 mm would be calculated as $\frac{7}{50}$ or 0.14.

If events are independent, the probability that they will occur in succession is a product of their individual probabilities (law of multiplication), e.g. the probability of soil being under 100 mm in depth is calculated at $0.14 \times 0.14 = 0.0196$.

Probability can be applied in many other different ways and is of fundamental importance to the geographer, particularly where sampling is necessary or information is incomplete.

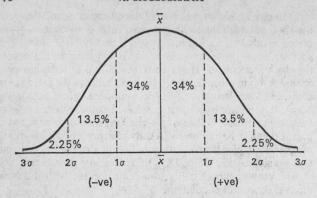

FIG. 47   *The normal distribution curve, showing the three areas of standard deviation (σ) from the mean.*

The area under the curve is unity and regarded as total probability. It may be used to calculate the probability that any individual item will appear above or below a given value.

By referring to the properties of a normal curve it is possible to make statements concerning the statistical probabilities of a certain result occurring when a sample is taken.

10. Mean deviation. This is a measure obtained by the average deviation of individual values from the mean of the distribution (*see* Table III):

$$\frac{\Sigma(x-\bar{x})}{n}$$

11. Standard deviation. Deviations from the mean are squared to eliminate negative values and summed. By dividing this value by the number of occurrences in the distribution (*n*), the variance is obtained. The standard deviation is then achieved by the following formula:

$$\sigma = \sqrt{\frac{\Sigma(x-\bar{x})^2}{n}} = 199.5$$

12. Z–score. The standard deviation can be used to show the probability of a certain value occurring in our study and this

TABLE III: SOIL DEPTHS IN SOUTH-WEST SURREY

x (mm)	$(x-\bar{x})$	$(x-\bar{x})^2$	x (mm)	$(x-\bar{x})$	$(x-\bar{x})^2$
24	442.7	195,894.7	440	26.7	712.9
86	380.7	144,932.5	448	18.7	349.7
121	345.7	119,508.5	454	12.7	161.3
135	331.7	110,024.9	465	1.7	2.9
147	319.7	102,208.1	472	−5.3	28.1
162	304.7	92,842.1	493	−26.3	691.7
191	275.7	76,010.5	514	−47.3	2,237.3
232	234.7	55,084.1	521	−54.3	2,948.5
240	226.7	51,393.9	527	−60.3	3,636.1
260	206.7	42,724.9	537	−70.3	4,942.1
274	192.7	37,133.3	556	−89.3	7,974.5
314	152.7	23,317.3	581	−114.3	13,064.5
323	143.7	20,649.7	592	−125.3	15,700.1
351	115.7	13,386.5	629	−162.3	26,341.3
369	97.7	9,545.3	631	−164.3	26,994.5
375	91.7	8,408.9	640	−173.3	30,032.9
384	82.7	6,839.3	646	−179.3	32,148.5
385	81.7	6,674.9	657	−190.3	36,214.1
394	72.7	5,184.5	697	−230.3	52,038.1
397	69.7	4,858.1	702	−235.3	55,366.1
404	62.7	3,931.3	757	−290.3	84,274.1
406	60.7	3,684.5	770	−303.3	91,990.8
408	58.7	3,445.7	794	−327.3	107,125.3
421	45.7	2,088.5	871	−404.3	163,458.5
437	29.7	882.1	925	−458.3	210,038.8

$$n = 50 \text{ and } \therefore \Sigma(x-\bar{x})^2 = 1,990,614.3$$
$$\bar{x} = 466.7$$

$$\therefore \sqrt{\frac{\Sigma(x-\bar{x})^2}{n}} = \pm199.5$$

$$= \text{Standard deviation}$$

probability is calculated as the Z–score from the formula:

$$Z = \frac{x-\bar{x}}{\sigma}$$

In the example below the chance of soil depths in our south-west Surrey study occurring between 300 mm and 500 mm is calculated.

The probability of soil samples being between 300 and 500 mm deep is calculated as follows:

$$\text{For 300 mm } Z = \frac{300-466.7}{199.5} = 0.84$$

$$\text{For 500 mm } Z = \frac{500-466.7}{199.5} = 0.17$$

The area under the normal curve falling between these two values represents the probability that a soil depth will fall between 300 and 500 mm. The probability is tabulated and may be found by consulting elementary statistical tables. The two values calculated will give probability values of:

For 300 mm with a Z–score of 0.84 probability = 0.294.
For 500 mm with a Z–score of 0.17 probability = 0.064.

The total probability is their sum, which equals 0.358. Therefore there is a 35.8% chance of soils occurring between our two critical depths. Figure 48 shows the probability of soil depths occurring between 300 and 500 mm represented by the area under the normal curve.

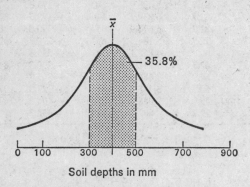

FIG. 48 *The probability of the occurrence of soil depths between 300 and 500 mm.*

13. Standard deviation and probability. Assuming our data has a normal distribution, then:

(*a*) approximately 68% of values in that sample will occur within one standard deviation (plus and minus) of the mean;

(*b*) approximately 95% of values in that sample will occur within two standard deviations (plus and minus) of the mean.

Thus the completed relationship between the normal curve of the distribution and the standard deviation of the data is as shown in Fig. 49.

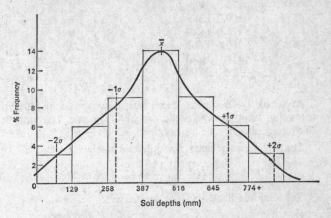

FIG. 49 *Standard deviations of sampled soil depths.*

14. Confidence limits. There is a small chance ($\triangle$ 1%) that the values in the sample will fall outside the ±3 standard deviation limits. These form confidence limits between which the geographer will work. Generally the geographer uses a 95% probability level (0.05), which means simply that the sample chosen will not be significantly different from the population under study five times out of a hundred, and will have no value in research. It will have occurred by chance only and not for sound geographical reasons.

15. Conclusions. Having taken a sample and made an analysis, the results should be a representation of the parent population. The confidence limits specify the relationship between sample and population but can only be calculated from the sample data. It is possible to work back from the sample results and estimate the minimum size of sample required for certain confidence limits at a given probability level.

EXAMPLE: The sizes of thirty woodlands in a specified area in southern England were surveyed and the frequency distribution calculated.

Size in hectares	Frequency
< 50	1
50.0– 74.9	2
75.0– 99.9	4
100.0–124.9	8
125.0–149.9	8
150.0–174.9	3
175.0–199.9	2
≤ 200	2
	30

A cumulative frequency curve was drawn based on this information using an arithmetic probability y axis. The straight line represents a normal distribution (*see* Fig. 50).

The average woodland size was determined by:

$$\bar{x} = \frac{\Sigma x}{n} = \frac{3,821.15}{30} = 127.4 \text{ hectares}$$

The total woodland area (the sample) was:

$$\Sigma x = 3,821.15 \text{ hectares}$$
$$\therefore \qquad \Sigma x^2 = 543,410 \text{ hectares}$$

The standard deviation of the sample was calculated from:

$$\sigma = \sqrt{\frac{\Sigma(x-\bar{x})^2}{n}} = 44.22 \text{ hectares}$$

This was applied to the distribution curve marking $\pm 1, 2,$ and 3 standard deviations away from the mean:

$$-3\sigma = -5.29 + 3\sigma = 260.03$$
$$-2\sigma = 38.93 + 2\sigma = 215.81$$
$$-1\sigma = 83.15 + 1\sigma = 171.59$$

The probability that a woodland area of an area lying between -1 and $+1$ will be sampled is 0.72 or 72% of all samples made, assuming the sampling was carried out randomly (*see* Fig. 51).

The value 72% was obtained from the constructed cumulative frequency curve as shown in Fig. 49.

When the data is not normally distributed it becomes necessary to apply techniques designed for skewed data to calculate these probability figures. The chi-squared test (χ^2) is one such test.

16. Chi-squared test (χ^2). This non-parametric test is designed to compare two distributions of geographical phenomena either (*a*) to prove that they both exist in the same population; or

(*b*) to compare an observed sample obtained from research with an expected sample which might occur under ideal circumstances.

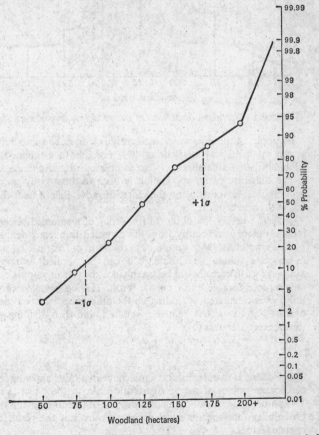

FIG. 50 *Cumulative frequency curve of woodland areas sampled in southern England.*

The *y*-axis has an arithmetic probability scale.

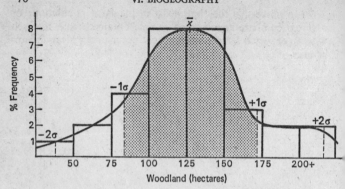

FIG. 51   *Standard deviations of sampled woodland areas.*

By applying the test, which incidently is subject to some quite severe mathematical restrictions, it is possible to estimate the probability that differences between samples are due to chance.

The difficulty of its application is under-estimated by many geographical textbooks, and therefore it is advisable to treat this test with some caution.

χ^2 tests whether the observed frequency of a sampled pheno- menon differs significantly from the expected frequency defined by the hypothesis. Data should be in the form of frequencies, not in absolute values, and although it can be applied to small samples (< 10) care should be taken since the size of sample can have a considerable effect on the result. Having sampled care- fully, χ^2 is calculated by adding up the differences between each observed and expected frequency squared, and then dividing by the expected frequency:

$$\chi^2 = \frac{\Sigma(O-E)^2}{E}$$

The χ^2 value is then tested for significance in a table showing the percentage points of the χ^2 distribution. As in the t test (VII, 17–18) the value is read off against degrees of freedom, giving the probability that the observed differences are not the result of chance factors.

17. Standard error of the mean. If it was possible to sample several sets of data from a population, then the distribution of all sample means should also follow a normal curve and be used just as the normal curve for one sample. Our researchers in Surrey may well have carried out a series of fifty soil depth samples and produced a wide range of mean values. Plotted, these would correspond to a normal distribution and the standard deviation of this distribution is known as the standard error of the mean.

Standard error of the mean = $S/\sqrt{n}$, where $S =$ standard deviation of the sample, and $n =$ sample size.

Using this statistical distribution it is possible to estimate the chance of the true mean of the population existing within certain limits of the sample means.

PROGRESS TEST 6

1. Discuss the flows within the carbon cycle and assess their influence on man. (2–3)

2. Draw a flow diagram explaining the processes within the soil system. (2–5)

3. What is a normal distribution, and which biogeographical phenomena may be distributed in a skewed manner? (7–10)

4. What is standard deviation and how is it related to probability? (9–14)

CHAPTER VII

Climatology and Meteorology

BACKGROUND

1. Definition. Climatology is the study of the average weather conditions of a place or region throughout the year. Meteorology is the science that investigates the atmosphere, in particular the physical processes that occur therein and the connected processes of the lithosphere and hydrosphere.

2. History of climatic data. Climatic observations were made by the ancient Greeks (Aristotle wrote about the climates in 350 B.C.) but accuracy in measurement and analysis has only been possible since the invention and availability of recording instruments and the development of the telegraph in the nineteenth century. Sequences of weather changes were correlated with barometric pressure systems both in time and space by pioneers in the subject such as Fitzroy and Abercrombie. The close study of low-level phenomena such as depressions by Bjerknes enabled meteorologists to understand the workings of the atmosphere and with the progress in scientific studies, the upper atmosphere circulations have also been partly explained. All this adds more and more to the confidence held in weather predictions. The Meteorological Office at Bracknell, Berkshire, receives information from all over the world and, by use of a computer, analyses the vast amount of data to provide valuable short- and long-term forecasts. This everyday information also gives new materials for research and the improvement of predictions.

It is, therefore, the increasing use of statistics and machinery that has improved the accuracy of meteorology, and contributed more reliable information to the study of the world's climates.

3. Problems in weather prediction. Climatic predictions have rarely been treated with confidence for two reasons:

(a) Measurements are often hard to take and errors are usually large.

78

(b) It is generally thought that the greater knowledge we have of past occurrences, the more reliability can be placed on prediction. As past records are very limited (London, for example, can only claim to have had official statistics from 1940) predictions are considered unreliable.

Climatic measurements were made in India in the fourth century B.C., and British rainfall figures exist for 1677. Records, however, are not continuous and hardly reliable.

COLLECTING CLIMATIC DATA—AN EXAMPLE

4. Rain-gauges. Even today inaccuracies occur through errors made in collection and measurement. The diagram in Fig. 52 shows the possible errors associated with rain gauges.

The use of rain gauges provides the geographer with a form of sampling (see III, 1–8). It would be necessary for the errors involved in measurement to be assessed to ensure that the most reliable results are used in further analysis. For this purpose, statistical tests of deviation can be applied (see VI, 8–14).

5. Rain gauge density. To cut down on errors arising from the location of gauges, it would be necessary to site a dense network of gauges over the area of study. This would prove impractical and costly. The World Meteorological Organisation, which attempts to standardise equipment, suggests a minimum density of precipitation networks depending on the environment. For example, small mountainous islands with irregular precipitation have a density of one gauge per 25 km². Great Britain has one in 39 km². In arid areas the density is as low as one gauge per 1500–10,000 km².

6. Siting rain gauges. The location of gauges is dependent also on the results and accuracy one is hoping to achieve. To obtain a fair representation of any area randomly-placed gauges would be statistically correct but even under this "fair" distribution clustering might occur and readings for the whole area would not be achieved. Remember, however, that any information, regardless of its quality, is better than none. It might be more logical, therefore, to deliberately site rain gauges so that as many as possible of the local variations within that area are covered. A variety of sites should be chosen providing data for lowland and highland sites, sheltered and exposed sites and rural and urban sites.

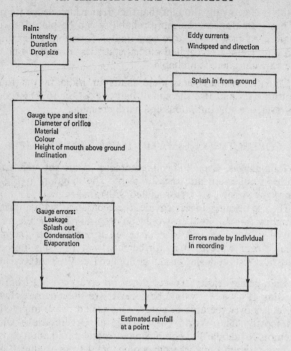

FIG. 52 *Factors affecting the accuracy of rain-gauge measurements.*

Why should the colour of the gauge be an important consideration in its design?

This might involve great cost and time which can be overcome by selecting sites randomly and using unbiased sampling methods to minimise effort.

7. **Thiessen polygons.** Having collected the data, its use and interpretation may then cause problems since the point measurements taken have to be extrapolated to represent an area rather than a precise, selected site. Thiessen polygons make some allowance for the uneven distribution of gauges throughout an area. They also incorporate data taken from adjacent areas of study (*see* Fig. 53).

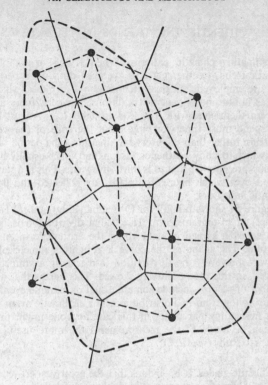

————— Lines joining adjacent gauges

————— Polygon perimeters drawn at right angles
           to bisect lines joining adjacent gauges

——— — Boundary of study area

FIG. 53 *Thiessen polygons.*

The idea is that, having constructed the Thiessen polygon network, each area delimited by the boundaries of the polygons is served by the rain gauge within that polygon. One assumes that the rainfall over the 12.7 cm hole of the rainfall gauge is similar over the whole of the polygonal area. Of course this is not strictly true; however, one is at least trying to quantify an otherwise confusing point distribution.

IDENTIFYING TRENDS IN CLIMATE

8. Estimating climatic patterns. When trying to establish a climatic trend, weather patterns averaged out over a period of time are employed, but this often irons out extremes, which are just as important as general conditions. Farmers, for example, concern themselves with frosts or droughts (e.g. August 1976), and spend more time worrying about the ends of the weather spectrum rather than the everyday situation. The period of time over which to study weather conditions and which usually ensures good, representative figures is thirty-five years. This is a standard period over which figures for places are collected and used as climatic indicators.

Figure 54 shows rainfall for (a) Padua (Italy) and (b) Helwan (Egypt) in histogram form. The Padua distribtuion is normal with an even spread of data about the arithmetic mean ($\bar{x}$)— 859 mm. The shape of the curve is roughly symmetrical. For Helwan, however, the distribution is markedly asymmetric or skewed, in this case positively skewed. This means that a large number of records include some unusual or extreme events that do not follow a normal distribution. The arithmetic mean would be a misleading parameter in this case and one might find the median or mode of the measurements the more useful parameters to study (see IV, 5).

9. Climatic guides. It is obvious that the great year-to-year variability of climate may conceal gradual trends from one century to the next.

These short-term fluctuations can be removed by the moving average technique. The method is to calculate average values for successive, overlapping periods of data.

In Table IV, years 1–10 are listed, together with the values of the statistic being investigated. A 5-yearly period is taken as sufficient from which to work out the average. The average at year 5 is $\frac{30}{5} = 6$ (total value of years 1 to 5, divided by 5). The next 5-yearly period (remember, over-lapping) is years 2–6, and the average here is 6.2. This process is then repeated for the 5-yearly periods 3–7, 4–8 and so on, and each average can be compared. This removes short-term fluctuations and any freak years.

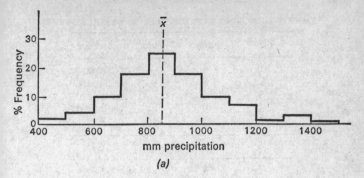

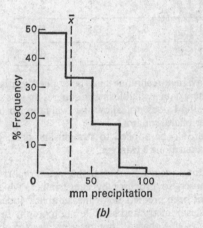

FIG. 54 *Rainfall figures in histogram form for (a) Padua, Italy and (b) Helwan, Egypt.*

Padua's figures show a normal distribution, while those for Helwan are positively skewed.

By calculating moving averages, changes in temperatures or rainfall may be seen in the form of a trend. Figure 55 shows that the longer the period of the moving average, the greater the amount of smoothing. An individual year in the period should be easy to find at the appropriate point of the period to which the average refers.

TABLE IV: MOVING AVERAGE OVER A 5-YEARLY PERIOD

Year	Value	Total	Average
1	4	—	No average
2	8	—	as 5 years
3	6	—	have not
4	9	—	yet lapsed
5	3	30	6.0
6	5	31	6.2
7	4	27	5.4
8	7	28	5.6
9	6	25	5.0
10	8	30	6.0

The moving average technique may be applied spatially (i.e. over an area) where data available in grid squares may be smoothed out. This method does not allow the evaluation of average values for the peripheral squares.

Smoothing can alo be applied to straight-line data, perhaps measurements taken along a transect.

10. Extreme natural events. Each year the media reports deaths and damage caused to property by catastrophes, which until recently have not been predictable or measurable. Modern techniques such as seismometry and satellite photography have provided warning systems that do not prevent disasters but give those affected areas a chance to prepare for the ensuing danger. Some unfortunate areas have few facilities to cope with natural forces and warnings often are not heeded or are too short. However, in many areas the loss of life or destruction of property can be limited. Climatic disasters are particularly hard to predict and in areas such as Bangladesh, the Sahel or Central America little can be done to lessen their impact.

The reliability of environmental conditions is always under question, for even farmers and tourists in moderate countries such as the United Kingdom have been confused by unusual weather conditions, particularly in recent years. The very dry

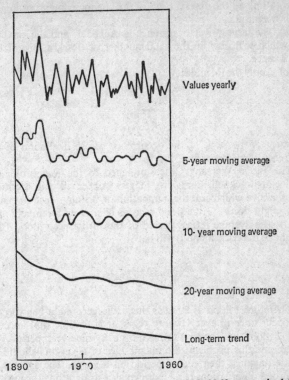

FIG. 55 *Rainfall figures for the U.K., 1890–1960, smoothed by different moving averages to show the long-term trend.*

summers of 1975 and 1976 and the autumn and winter gales of 1975 and 1977 created huge problems for the individual and nation as a whole. Potato shortages, the result of dry growing-periods, led to extra imports from Poland and India.

11. Return periods. How likely is a crop failure? What will be the extent of a flood or the strength of a gale? These questions can be answered to some degree of accuracy by a return, or recurrence, period calculation. This is the average interval within which one event of a certain size can be expected to occur. The method of calculation is as follows:

(a) Rank all the observations of the phenomenon according to their magnitude.

(b) The largest ever occurrence is ranked 1, and the smallest N, which will also be the total number of observations of the occurrence.

(c) Apply the formula:

$$\frac{N+1}{r}$$

where r is the rank of the occurrence whose likelihood of recurrence you want to find.

The Flood Warning Office, attached to the Meteorological Office at Bracknell, Berkshire, may be concerned with a critical flood above which size the inundation of Britain's eastern coastline might occur. Given flood records of a river for ninety-nine years, the average return period of the fifth largest flood (this might be the critical flood) will be:

$$\frac{99+1}{5} = 20 \text{ years}$$

Therefore a flood as large as this, or larger, might be expected to occur once in every twenty years. It is feasible that an even larger flood will occur during the ninety-nine-year period. To overcome this problem, the magnitudes of all events should be plotted against their return period on a graph. The average of recorded observations can be drawn as a straight line through all the observations. From this it is possible to estimate the most likely return ratios based on all the data available (see Fig. 56).

12. Prediction. The line, when extended, gives the predicted size of the greatest flood likely to occur within a century. This estimation gives some idea of the size of flood possible, and preparation for this flood should be made. However, the 200-year flood may occur at any time during the period. Indeed, it may even occur twice in the period. In this event, another 200-year flood would not be expected again on the average for 199 years.

Man cannot perfect a method of prediction, but he is at least making efforts to prepare himself against the forces of nature and the likelihood of disasters.

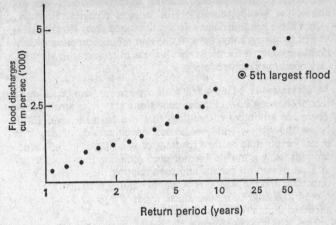

FIG. 56 *Return periods of floods.*

MICRO-CLIMATES

13. Man and climate. Climate is an important influence on man, his life-style and prosperity. Man, in turn, is capable of altering climates, minimally at first but now on such a scale that world organisations are restricting pollution, development and environmental change in order to stem the amount of chemical elements and excessive heat entering the earth's immediate atmosphere (the troposphere).

Man's initial attempts to control or alter climate have been by simple heating and irrigation processes. Sweden now spends over five per cent of her national income on fuels and insulation. With industrialisation, the amount of smog and dust in the air within urban areas has increased beyond comfort. London's inhabitants found in the early 1950s that "pea-soup" fogs caused illness and death. About 11,000 people were affected in 1951 and 1952.

More recently, determined efforts have been made to cause rain to fall earlier by cloud seeding with silver iodide. Fog dissipation around airports and lightning control are two other ways that the physical processes of the atmosphere have been altered.

Man is partially responsible for climatic change, but it is over small or micro-areas that he has provided more sweeping changes.

Generally, geographers talk in terms of climatic zones—for example, the Mediterranean or the tropical climates. However, within these zonal divisions lie small, unique areas that are controlled by topography, flora, fauna and other local effects. Geographers concern themselves with these micro-areas as they are very relevant to man's behaviour.

14. Experiments. Many worthwhile experiments can be set up at school showing how climatic conditions vary over small areas. There are a number of readings that can be made, and **15–18** below shows how windspeeds vary on either side of a hill. It might be possible to take readings of windspeeds in the school grounds using a mobile anemometer, sampling four times a day at a set of control points, and then relating the results to wind directions and the positions of school buildings. In many schools there will always be a notoriously windy playground and a calm sheltered spot in the lee of a building.

The whirling hygrometer is easily used and interpreted, measuring relative humidity of the air. These readings will give vital clues to the moisture content of the air near buildings, lakes or out in the country.

In a simple experiment, students may show how air temperatures vary, being controlled by the surroundings and the type of surface of the sample area. By setting up a number of permanent thermometers or by using the dry bulb of the whirling hygrometer, it should be possible to make readings at several control points about the school over a period of time. By using the whirling hygrometer along a transect line away from the centre of the school buildings towards the periphery, readings could be taken every ten metres. Five readings at each control point would give an average figure, which could then be plotted on to a map of the school. By joining up the sample points that had the same temperature readings, an isoline map (*see* II, 7) would result. The existence of a "heat island" may be proven and also anomalous readings could be explained.

FIELD-STUDY OF A MICRO-CLIMATE

15. Objective. To illustrate the kind of study that might be made on a micro-scale, the following exercise was carried out to compare windspeeds on the windward and leeward sides of a small hill. By applying a statistical test, it was possible to show quantitatively that one sample (the windward) was significantly different from the other sample (the leeward).

16. Comparisons. Even though some comparisons may be made, it is possible that a correlation between samples will occur simply by chance, and the results from statistical tests are therefore considered not statistically significant. To prove significance there are tests designed to suit the method of comparison. For a purely descriptive comparison, the standard error of the difference may be employed. Correlations may be tested by fitting confidence limits to regression lines and the chi-squared test (χ^2) is particularly reliable for inferential theoretical explanation.

17. Student's *t* test. For either purely descriptive comparisons or correlations the Student's *t* test can be used. This test can be applied to show the significant difference of the null hypothesis—that a sample, A, is similar to another sample, B.

When the parameters of a population are known, it is possible to describe the form of the sampling distribution of sample means. The Student's *t* test will permit the testing of hypotheses with samples drawn from normally-distributed populations when it is not known. These distributions are known as the *t* distributions.

Similar to the *Z* statistic (*see* VI, **12**), both are expressed as a deviation of a sample mean from a population mean (known or hypothesized) in terms of the standard error of the mean. By reference to the appropriate sampling distribution we may express this deviation in terms of a probability. The *t* statistic has a family of distribution that vary as a function of the degrees of freedom (d.f.). If there were four numbers which had a restriction that they must sum to 100, and three of these were allowed to vary, then the fourth number must have a fixed value. The degrees of freedom in this case is $N-1$. When we deal with *two* samples, the degrees of freedom will equal the number of items in the two samples, minus two.

Two types of *t* test can be employed:

(*a*) When samples A and B are independent (unrelated), a weak form of the test can be used. Not much reliance can be placed on this.

(*b*) When samples A and B are represented as paired data. This test is much stronger, and the significance of the difference between each pair of observations is measured. The difference between each pair of observations is known as *d*.

Using this second method a simple application of the technique can be applied to climatic data.

18. Comparing two samples. It is useful to compare two samples to estimate how significantly different they are. The windspeeds exercise was designed to test readings made at stations A and B (*see* Fig. 57).

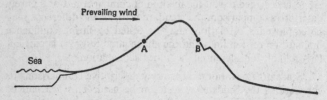

FIG. 57   *Positions of the stations chosen to sample windspeeds.*

TABLE V: AVERAGE WINDSPEEDS, AT STATIONS A AND B, FOR
FIFTEEN YEARS, SELECTED AT RANDOM FROM A PERIOD OF
RECORD OF FORTY-FIVE YEARS

Station A (windward) km/hr	Station B (leeward) km/hr	d (difference, X − Y) km/hr	d^2
39.8	39.0	+0.8	0.64
29.5	29.1	+0.4	0.16
23.2	23.2	+0.0	0.0
30.2	30.1	+0.1	0.01
29.8	29.3	+0.5	0.25
20.1	20.4	−0.3	0.09
28.1	27.9	+0.2	0.04
40.5	39.4	+1.1	1.21
33.5	32.9	+0.6	0.36
26.9	27.0	−0.1	0.01
31.0	30.6	+0.4	0.16
18.3	18.7	−0.4	0.16
30.4	29.9	+0.5	0.25
43.7	42.5	+1.2	1.44
37.4	36.3	+1.1	1.21
$\Sigma d = 6.1$	$d = 0.41$		$\Sigma d^2 = 5.99$

The samples chosen for use in the t test must be selected randomly (see III, 2–8) and be distributed normally about the mean.

The average annual windspeeds have been calculated in km/hr at the two stations for a forty-five-year period. A random sample of fifteen years' observations has been made from each station. It is desired to know whether or not the windspeeds at A generally exceed those at B (i.e. whether or not the two samples are significantly different).

From the paired observations the difference (d) between A and B in each of the fifteen years may be calculated by simple subtraction. At this point a check is made to ensure that the values of d are normally distributed. If not, the t test cannot be employed and it will be necessary to employ a non-parametric test.

The values of d are ranked according to size and then placed into classes. The number of classes is determined by the formula:

$$k = 1 + 3.3 \, (\log n) \text{ where } n = \text{number of observations.}$$

In this case $n = 15$, and $k = 5$, approximately. The d values are classified as shown in Table VI.

TABLE VI: CLASSIFICATION OF d

Class	Frequency	% of total	Cumulative total
−0.4– −0.1	3	20	20
0.0– +0.3	3	20	40
0.4– 0.7	5	33	73
0.8– 1.1	3	20	93
1.2– 1.5	1	7	100

The cumulative total is then plotted using an arithmetic probability y axis and should give an approximately straight line if normality occurs (see Fig. 58).

If the differences are not shown to be normally distributed then a stronger test is employed—the chi-squared test (χ^2—see VI, 16).

The next step is to set a level of probability to which one is allowed to work. Geographers often use the 5% (0.05) level, which means that for 5% of the time the hypothesis cannot be

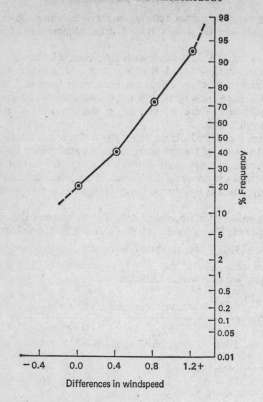

FIG. 58 *Cumulative frequency curve of differences in windspeeds (d), using an arithmetic probability y-axis.*

The distribution of differences is normal if the line obtained is approximately straight.

accepted and a new hypothesis must be devised. The graph in Fig. 59 shows the 5% levels.

The *t* test determines under which parts of the graph the hypothesis lies. For 5% of the time, the hypothesis cannot be accepted.

Now the data is applied to the formula:

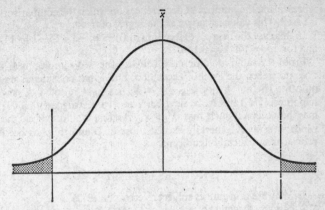

FIG. 59 *Normal distribution curve showing 5% levels of significance.*

$$t = \frac{\text{mean } d}{\sqrt{\dfrac{\text{sum of the squares of } d}{n-1}}} \times \sqrt{\frac{1}{n}}$$

NOTE: Sum of the squares of $d =$

$$\Sigma d^2 - \left[\frac{(\Sigma d)^2}{n}\right]$$

$n =$ numbers of observations

$\therefore t$ value $= 3.146$

This value has to be compared to a table of t observations devised under ideal conditions. These tables can be found in most statistical textbooks. The extract below shows the critical values used to test the significance of our t value:

d.f.	0.05 *probability*	0.01 *probability*
12	2.179	3.055
13	2.160	3.012
14	2.145	2.977
15	2.131	2.947

The smaller the sample, the greater the difference between the means must be (and the higher the value of t) to reach a given level of significance. It is necessary, therefore, to select a value representing the number of occurrences on which the comparison is based. This value is known as the degree of freedom.

In this case the degrees of freedom (d.f.) $= n - 1 = 15 - 1 = 14$, and for d.f. $= 14$, $t = 3.146$.

From the table the difference between the two samples means does not reach the level of acceptance and is not considered significant. The null hypothesis $\bar{X}_A = \bar{X}_B$ has to be rejected. A new hypothesis (H_1) has to be devised. The t values suggest that H_1 may be accepted such that $\bar{X}_A > \bar{X}_B$. As one would expect, the windspeeds at A generally exceed those at B and this has been proved as statistically significant.

PROGRESS TEST 7

1. Why are rain gauges subject to errors? (3–7)
2. Discuss the value of predictions. (12)
3. Why do microclimates present valuable topics for study? (13, 14)
4. What is the Student's t test, and what conditions must be met before it is used? (17, 18)

CHAPTER VIII

Urban Geography

DIFFICULTIES OF DELIMITATION

1. Definition. Urban geography means the study of towns or cities. These two words are almost synonymous to geographers, though a city would tend to be larger than a town. However, there is no clearly defined and generally accepted division between the two. It is perhaps best to say that, for a variety of reasons, many of which are historical, a city is a town that has been designated a city by being given a charter by one of the country's rulers.

Thirty per cent of the world's population live in urban areas, and over eighty per cent of the population of the U.K. is urban. One of the great problems facing studies of urban geography is the decision about exactly where the urban area ends. In Britain, some rural areas may contain commuters who travel to towns to work, or may simply be an extension of an urban area across an administrative boundary. There are problems of this nature in a study of British urban areas, even though Britain is very well documented. In other parts of the world the answer to this kind of problem may be less easily discovered.

There is also the problem of defining *urban*. Is it where the solid continuous mass of buildings ends, or does it include ribbon settlements? Should it be an area with more than a certain number of people, such as a hectare? Different countries employ different definitions for their census returns, and these serve to emphasise the problems.

(a) *U.K.* —more than 4 people per hectare.
(b) *Denmark* —over 200 in a settlement.
(c) *France* —over 2,000 in a settlement.
(d) *India* —over 5,000 in a settlement.

2. Measurement. The difficulties of defining the boundaries of urban areas may be overcome by using precise measuring techniques, and this is an important aspect of quantitative geography. If a map was divided into a series of measured areas, exact numbers of people per square could be counted (*see* Fig. 60) or the number of houses in each block could be counted and, by using an average figure of, say, four people per house, the population density could be shown.

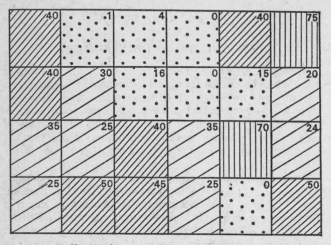

FIG. 60 *Grid squares showing population density.*

Different shadings represent different densities and figures show the exact number of people per square.

There are many problems—for example, shopping streets may contain shops with no permanent residents, or buildings may be blocks of flats and not single or simple dwellings. Therefore, field-studies would be necessary to provide additional information to ensure the accuracy of this technique.

The collection of information in the field, or rather the street, as required in the previous example, could be continued to cover the whole built-up area. By means of a street-by-street survey, a land-use map of the urban area could be compiled (*see* Fig. 61). In this type of study, the problem of scale would be encountered. For example, if an entire large urban area were being studied, the urban centre might simply be classified as the central business district. However, if a more detailed map were required of the various services and shops in the centre, a different type of classi-fication would be necessary (*see* Fig. 62).

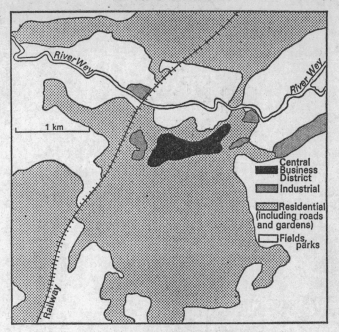

FIG. 61   *Land-use map of Godalming.*

3. Central business district. The central business district (C.B.D.) is that part of an urban area which contains the shops, business concerns and offices. In the U.S.A. it is referred to as the downtown area, and in the U.K. it is the shopping centre or simply town centre and its immediate environs.

For a detailed study of the C.B.D., each building will have to be plotted on a map, and for this scale of work a clear key will be essential (*see* II, **6**). In any form of map work, a key which contains, say, five items is simpler and easier to compile or read than a map with fifty items. A large number of items gives much more information and accuracy—two big advantages, but it is more difficult to compile and also understand at a glance—two big disadvantages. Therefore the time available for the study together with the requirements of the end product are important when assessing the scale of study to be made.

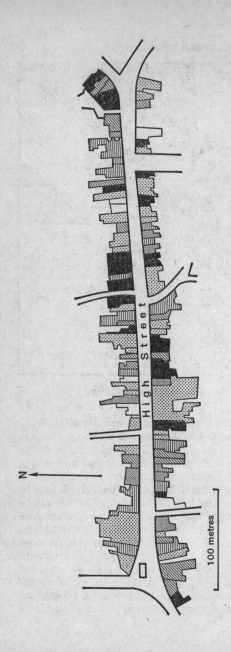

Food and drink retail outlets

Clothes and shoe shops

Services (banks, restaurants, pubs, hairdressers)

Professional services (opticians, estate agents)

Consumer goods (hardware, furniture, electrical goods)

Vacant

FIG. 62 *Detailed land-use map of the centre (or central business district) of Godalming.*

N

High Street

100 metres

URBAN MORPHOLOGY

The map of Godalming shows a real town, but as each and every town is slightly different from all others, it is useful to have a few standard ideas that are applicable to most or all towns. The three most useful ideas are based on the work of Burgess, Hoyt, and Harris and Ullman.

4. Burgess. Burgess studied Chicago in the late 1920s, and found a series of concentric zones of development. He thought that similar zones would occur in most towns. As towns grow, they spread outwards and are therefore dynamic and not static phenomena. The old town centre would be surrounded by a zone in transition, in which the old houses would be replaced by industrial or business properties. The residential zone would be pushed further out from the town centre, and beyond would be other zones of different standard housing (*see* Fig. 63).

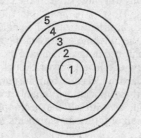

1. Central business district
2. Zone of change
3. Zone of workers' homes
4. Residential
5. Commuter

FIG. 63 *Burgess's concentric-circle model of urban development.*

5. Hoyt. This is clearly too much of a simplification, but most towns do show some signs of a circular pattern though it is normally rather patchy. Hoyt's studies of American towns during the late 1930s led him to draw a sector town, to show that many towns grow with non-concentric zones, because of the influence of major routeways. These help to give a star-like shape to the growth of some urban areas as shown in Fig. 64, which portrays Hoyt's model.

6. Harris and Ullman. Harris and Ullman, in the 1940s, showed that multiple-nuclei growth was also important, as in Fig. 65. They believed that special functions, or the absorption of small, old

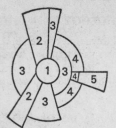

1. Central business district
2. Industry — along routeways
3. Cheaper housing
4. Medium-priced housing
5. Expensive housing

FIG. 64 *Hoyt's sector theory of urban development.*

villages or neighbouring towns would create a much more irregular and patchy zoning.

7. Basis for study. All three models are oversimplifications, but they have become the standard models for the study of urban morphology, and provide a good starting point or basis for the study of any urban area. All towns will show some of the characteristics emphasised by Burgess, Hoyt or Ullman, but all will show uniqueness. Careful studies in urban areas will enable the geographer to explain many of the differences between the town under consideration and those outlined in these standard models. Some pattern or zoning is apparent in all towns though not necessarily as clearly as the standard models of urban morphology suggest. However, a study of these models will enable understanding of urban growth, and, as with all the geographical models, may help in the prediction of future developments. Each

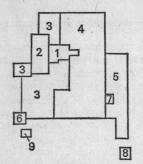

1. Central business district
2. Manufacturing
3. Cheaper housing
4. Medium-priced housing
5. Expensive housing
6. Heavy industry
7. Subsidiary central business district
8. Outlying residential area
9. Outlying industrial area

FIG. 65 *Harris and Ullman's multiple-nuclei theory of urban development.*

town is different because of historical factors, local physical factors such as hills, rivers or coastlines, or simply culture, traditions and economic standards in the country. Also, each town is different when compared with other towns near by due to its size.

HIERARCHY OF SETTLEMENTS

8. Size of cities. Size may be measured in terms of total area or by population. Tokyo (11 million), New York (8 million) are probably the two largest towns in population, but both Kiruna in Arctic Sweden and Los Angeles in California are larger towns in area. These examples really show that a vague classification of towns by *size* is very unsatisfactory; a consideration of towns containing skyscrapers in the U.S.A., (high-density population with small area) as compared with single-storey buildings for example in New Zealand (low-density population over a large area) would confirm this opinion.

Even the use of size based on population numbers has problems, because there are different methods of compiling these figures. For example, London has a population of 8 million, or 2.8 million or 7,000. The City of London contains only 7,000 permanent inhabitants, though there are over one million workers in the City. The Inner London boroughs contain 2.8 million and Greater London has over 7 million people. Even this last figure is open to variation because it is by no means certain just how far London extends and which towns in Surrey, Kent, Essex, Hertfordshire, etc., should be included within Greater London. Many towns in the world will have two widely differing, but correct, population figures, for the city proper and for the greater urban area.

9. Classification of towns. Classification by population does pose problems, but nevertheless population is useful and measurable; it is much more satisfactory than saying "large" towns or "small" towns. A large town is sometimes defined as an urban area with over 1 million people, or sometimes over 100,000.

Large towns can be classified in a quantitative fashion. Importance here will not be determined *purely* by population, but also by the town's relationship with the surrounding area. For example, Alice Springs is a very large town because of the sparsity of population in the surrounding area. Towns of similar size in the U.K., such as Ulverston in Lancashire or Thetford in

Norfolk, are of apparent insignificance when compared to their surrounding areas and towns.

In order to devise a useful classification of urban areas, definite population numbers have to be chosen. For example, in the U.K. there are (figures for town and not metropolitan area):

(*a*) two towns with more than one million inhabitants;
(*b*) six towns with more than 500,000 inhabitants;
(*c*) twenty-nine towns with more than 250,000 inhabitants;
(*d*) ninety-one towns with more than 100,000 inhabitants.

10. Orders of towns. The list in **9** above contains fairly arbitrary divisions, but it can be used to rank towns into those of first order (over one million), second order (over 500,000), and third order (over 250,000). This hierarchy of settlements is a useful quantitative technique.

Hierarchies of settlements may also be based on certain services, activities or functions in the urban areas. These may be studied by reference to the *Yellow Pages* of telephone directories. This will again enable a hierarchy of urban areas to be compiled. This may closely follow that based purely upon population, but there are likely to be some differences, and knowledge of the area will probably allow these differences to be explained.

11. Yellow pages. The hierarchy of urban areas may be assessed by the number of shops, banks, etc., located in a town. Reference to *Yellow Pages* will provide information such as appears below:

	Guildford	*Aldershot*	*Godalming*	*Haslemere*
Number of				
Banks	21	6	8	7
Dentists	18	8	5	4
Florists	6	6	3	3
Shoe shops	11	6	3	2
Fish-and-chip shops	4	10	4	1

The population of these four towns are—Guildford (56,000), Aldershot (33,000), Godalming (18,000) and Haslemere (13,000), and the number of services or shops should be related to the population of the town. Many other factors may be influential, such as the proximity of local villages that may be within the catchment area (or sphere of influence, *see* **13** below), thereby swelling the total population. Also, not all establishments will be listed in *Yellow Pages*, and many towns are of markedly different character, according to tradition, wealth or activities within the local area. For example, the four towns listed above contain Aldershot, a military town, and Haslemere, a market and commuter town.

12. Functional centrality value. Functional centrality values (F.C.V.) may be discovered for each function and then a settlement index (S.I.) may be discovered for each town. Both the F.C.V. and the S.I. provide quantitative information that will enable valid comparisons to be made.

The F.C.V. is obtained by totalling the number of outlets of one particular type in the four towns concerned, e.g. 42 banks. Using the formula $\frac{1}{42} \times 100$ will give an answer of 2.4, which is the F.C.V. for banks.

In a similar way, four other F.C.V.s may be obtained:

$$\text{Dentists} \qquad \frac{1}{35} \times 100 = 2.8$$

$$\text{Florists} \qquad \frac{1}{18} \times 100 = 5.5$$

$$\text{Shoe shops} \qquad \frac{1}{22} \times 100 = 4.5$$

$$\text{Fish and chip shops} \; \frac{1}{19} \times 100 = 5.2$$

In order to discover the S.I. for each town, multiply the F.C.V. as listed above, by the number of outlets in that town, and add the totals together, e.g., for Guildford:

21 banks	$\times 2.4 =$	50.4
18 dentists	$\times 2.8 =$	50.4
6 florists	$\times 5.5 =$	33.0
11 shoe shops	$\times 4.5 =$	49.5
4 fish-and-chip shops	$\times 5.2 =$	20.8
	Total	204.1

The S.I. for Guildford is 204, and the same process will reveal the S.I. for the other three towns. The information can all be drawn up in a graph using the settlement index as the vertical axis and rank order of the town (i.e. population) for the horizontal axis (*see* Fig. 66).

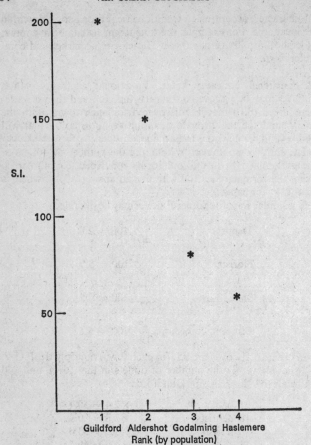

FIG. 66 *Settlement indices for four Surrey towns.*

Towns of similar sizes located in different regions may also be compared by reference to *Yellow Pages*. For example, Guildford and Crewe both have similar populations but are different in character. Guildford is a market and shopping centre in a commuting area, and is a university town. Crewe is a railway and industrial town.

	Banks	Dentists	Florists	Shoe shops	Fish-and-chip shops
Guildford	21	18	6	11	4
Crewe	8	9	5	8	26

This gives information about the different character of the two towns.

13. Sphere of influence or catchment area. Each town has its area of influence, rather like the hinterland of a port. This is called its sphere of influence or catchment area (it can also be called umland or urban field). Each sphere of influence is likely to spread around the urban area to include several square kilometres of surrounding countryside. This is explained by reference to Christaller's central place theory.

CENTRAL PLACE THEORY

14. Christaller. It is well known that shops attract customers from the surrounding area, and the catchment area of a shop is likely to be roughly circular, enclosing everyone within easy reach of the shop. In former centuries, to be within easy reach meant within walking distance, but nowadays transport is more speedy.

Walter Christaller studied the size and spacing of settlements in his home area of southern Germany and wrote about this in 1933. What he described was the central place theory, in which all settlements, or central places, serve the surrounding countryside. The functions of the settlements will attract people and the larger the settlement is, the greater will be its number of functions, and hence its power of attracting people. The smallest settlements will only satisfy primary or daily requirements, such as a loaf of bread, whereas larger settlements will satisfy primary daily requirements, but also more occasional need. These may include quality clothes, good schools and medical consultants.

15. Hexagons. The catchment areas should be circles, but it is impossible to draw a series of circles without overlapping, or leaving gaps (see Fig. 67). Mathematically, hexagons provide the best-fitting shape and so the central place theory is very closely associated with the hexagon. In southern Germany, Christaller found that each small town attracted people from a surrounding area that approximated to a hexagon in shape. For every six small towns, there would be a bigger town with more specialised

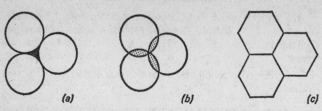

FIG. 67 *Shapes for catchment areas.*

Circles are inappropriate, as they leave gaps (*a*) or overlap (*b*). Hexagons are more appropriate (*c*).

functions, and thus a hierarchy of settlements would develop. The small first-order settlements in southern Germany were roughly seven kilometres apart, whereas the second-order settlements were roughly twelve kilometres apart.

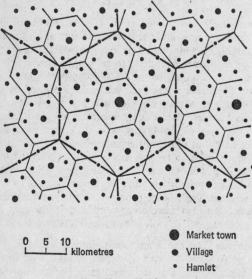

0   5   10   kilometres

● Market town
● Village
· Hamlet

FIG. 68 *Christaller hexagons.*

Inside the larger hexagons (showing the catchment areas of the market towns) are smaller hexagons showing the catchment areas of the villages. Settlements coinciding with boundary lines belong to the catchment areas on both sides of the line.

The starting point for Christaller was an assumption that a certain area of land will support an urban settlement that will provide essential services. He also assumed that people had uniform purchasing power, that there was an even distribution of population and that transport facilities were equal in all directions. Physical features needed to be minimal and a flat featureless plain (an isotropic surface) was ideal. These conditions could never be met in full but the theory provides a model, or a basic idea, for study. The model can be used to study any area, and the divergences from the simplified version, or model, may be explained by local features.

16. Lösch. The Christaller hexagons may be drawn in a variety of ways to enclose different numbers of settlements (*see* Fig. 68). In 1954, a German economist called Lösch adjusted Christaller's ideas in an attempt to make them approach reality more closely. He showed that the bigger centres provided specialised services—that is, services with a larger threshold, but they also served local needs such as daily perishable foods. Lösch superimposed the hexagons in such a way that the hamlet (first-order settlement),

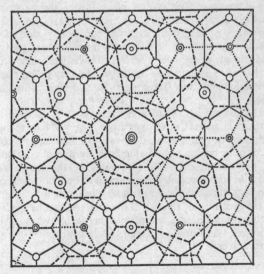

FIG. 69 *Lösch's theory of catchment areas.*

the village (second-order settlement) and town (third-order settlement) all centre on one point. This showed that some sections of the landscape contained many more settlements than occurred in other sections, and this actually resembled reality more closely than the absolute equality of Christaller (*see* Fig. 69).

17. Intra-urban hierarchy. The hierarchy of settlements as outlined with reference to areas of country, may also be applicable to large cities. A city will have its central business district containing much of the commerce and most of the large shops. Several places in the suburbs may have small clusters of shops or a street containing a variety of basic requirements. Additionally, even smaller clusters, of two or three shops, may be found on busy street corners, such as where a main road from the city centre crosses a ring road. Finally, there will be the occasional isolated shop, such as a new housing estate or an old shop from a small hamlet which has been swallowed up by urban growth (*see* Fig. 70).

18. Advantages and disadvantages of the basic central place theory.

(*a*) *Advantages.* The central place theory shows clearly the idea of hierarchy of settlement, and goes a long way to explain the distribution of settlement and the continuous idea of urban growth. It can be shown to have some relevance to all parts of the world though never with a perfect fit. The basic model can be constructed to demonstrate the theory and may be adjusted to fit any real-life situation. The model also has some value for prediction.

(*b*) *Disadvantages.* Christaller really only considered service centres and ignored the fact that urban areas will have many more functions. For example, the discovery of minerals, the growth of port or other communication facilities, the arrival of urban overspill population, etc., will all complicate the simple pattern. Christaller also assumed the landscape to be a homogeneous environment, or an isotropic surface. Variations in relief features and the locations of rivers will obviously affect the distribution of settlements. So, too, will many other factors such as climatic conditions, variations in soil type and the availability of transport and resources.

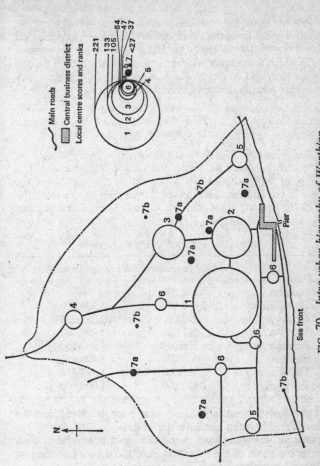

FIG. 70 *Intra-urban hierarchy of Worthing.*
Local centres are ranked according to the number of shops and services they contain.

RANKING

19. Primate town. It is possible that the largest town, often the capital, will influence the entire country. Large towns are called primate towns. Towns can be ranked in order of size of population in which the primate will be number one, the second biggest number two, and so on. In the U.K. (defining the town by its town limits and not metropolitan area) the order is:

1. London.
2. Birmingham.
3. Glasgow.

20. Rank-size rule. Zipf devised a theory, now referred to as the rank-size rule, which suggested that second ranked towns in a country or region should have a population one-half that of the largest town, and the third ranked should only be one-third the size of the primate. This does not fit the U.K. population figures very closely (*see* Table VII).

TABLE VII: U.K. POPULATION FIGURES

	Actual population	*Expected population*
London	7,168,000	—
Birmingham	1,003,000	3,584,000
Glasgow	816,000	2,389,333
Liverpool	561,000	1,792,000
Manchester	516,000	1,433,600
Sheffield	507,000	1,194,666
Leeds	499,000	1,194,666
Edinburgh	450,000	1,024,000

These figures obviously show a very poor fit indeed, and the reason for this is the excessive size of London. The capital has become so dominant that its relative growth has been much greater than that of the other towns. If the size of London was 2,250,000, the expected population figures, according to the rank-size rule, would be:

Birmingham	1,125,000	Sheffield	375,000
Glasgow	750,000	Leeds	321,428
Liverpool	562,500	Edinburgh	281,250
Manchester	450,000		

If the size of London was 3,000,000, the corresponding figures would be: 1,500,000; 1,000,000; 750,000; 600,000; 500,000; 428,571; 375,000, which give an even better fit.

The lack of exact comparison does not disprove the theory because, as with all theories or models, it provides a starting point for study. The hypothesis can be studied, analysed and discrepancies explained. An urban area that is much larger than its expected population may be a capital, located on a coal-field or on a navigable estuary, but an obvious reason will generally be found to explain the unexpected growth.

Ranking may take place on any scale, and is not restricted to a nation. A county or a local district may have its settlements ranked, and a study of the area will generally allow unexpected figures to be explained.

21. Local studies. Local settlements may be ranked according to population or according to information extracted from *Yellow Pages*. It is interesting to measure the spheres of influence of the settlements and this may be attempted by several methods. Amongst the methods which may be employed are:

(*a*) the delivery distance of the shops;
(*b*) bus services;
(*c*) study of shopping visits;
(*d*) the delivery rounds of milkmen;
(*e*) newspaper readership;
(*f*) catchment areas of schools or hospitals.

These will involve the use of different geographical techniques for collecting and analysing information.

ATTRACTION OF URBAN AREAS

22. Assessment of spheres of influence. Newspaper readership can be studied by sales of papers from the head office, if figures are readily available. Another method to extract information from a newspaper involves reading through and listing the number of settlements that are mentioned and the frequency with which the name appears. For example, a *Surrey Advertiser* from the Guildford area mentioned Guildford thirty-eight times, Godalming sixteen times, and many other small settlements. All the localities mentioned could be plotted on a map to show one version of

Guildford's sphere of influence. The map could be based on all the entries in the newspaper or merely a selection of items, such as the advertisements or the births, marriages and deaths sections.

The distribution of newspapers may depend on historical factors, or the personal energy and effort of one proprietor, but will give some indication of the sphere of influence. The study of milk deliveries will also give helpful information without providing a perfect answer. A map based on a regional milk-centre and showing the delivery routes of individual lorries will be useful.

23. Other spheres of influence. Just as the milk-delivery rounds may be mapped, using the town or village under consideration as the main point, or central place, so too may bus services. Bus timetables contain information to show how many buses travel to neighbouring towns or villages each day. The frequency can be shown by a flow-line diagram (*see* XI, **16**), which will give a very speedy impression of major routes but will also show the sphere of influence of the town. This sphere may advantageously be subdivided into an area of major influence and an area of lesser influence.

Other methods of establishing the sphere of influence or catchment areas of towns will be based on homes of children travelling to a particular school, or the homes of people treated by a hospital. The delivery range of certain shops may also be useful as might the range of territory covered by estate agents in the properties they handle. All of these methods are useful, though never perfect, because of local or human influences. For instance, some good independent schools might draw from an exceptionally-large catchment area (*see* Fig. 71). Local-authority boundaries may also dictate that children from a wide area attend a school in a specific town. This is emphasised in rural areas, where a small town may have a catchment area covering many square kilometres, whereas a similar-size school in a large town may have a much smaller catchment area.

Hospitals may specialise in treatment of particular complaints and, therefore, the catchment area for certain ailments will be greater than that for all forms of treatment. Deliveries by shops will also be varied. For example, Harrods deliver over a very wide area in southern England to give a large catchment area. Bentalls of Kingston also deliver over a wide area to show a larger sphere

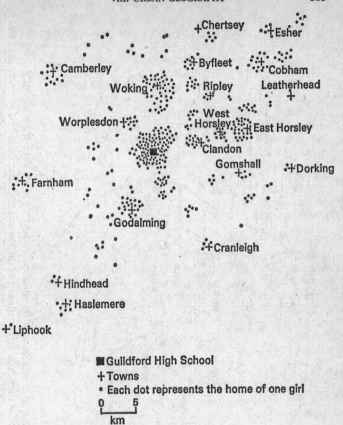

FIG. 71 *Catchment area of Guildford High School for Girls.*

of influence than would generally apply to the town of Kingston (*see* Fig. 72).

Consideration has been given to individual catchment areas, but how do these fit together on a regional or national scale? Figure 73 shows this with reference to Marks and Spencer. The map shows the similarities between the distribution of Marks and Spencer and the distribution of population. All large towns contain a branch, and smaller towns—with less than 30,000 inhabit-

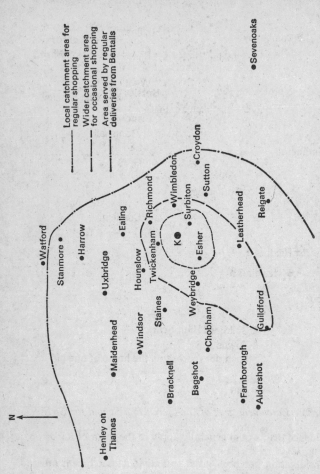

Local catchment area for
regular shopping

Wider catchment area
for occasional shopping

Area served by regular
deliveries from Bentalls

FIG. 72 *Catchment area of Kingston shopping centre and the area covered by Bentalls' store.*
The areas are constricted to the east and north-east as the influence of London increases here.

ants—do so too, if they are located in a rural area or in a tourist area, in which case the catchment area for local customers will be greater than the resident urban population.

The spheres of influence for individual functions within one town may be quite different, but if the different functions are superimposed on top of each other, an average may be delimited. This is an interesting and worthwhile exercise for any town.

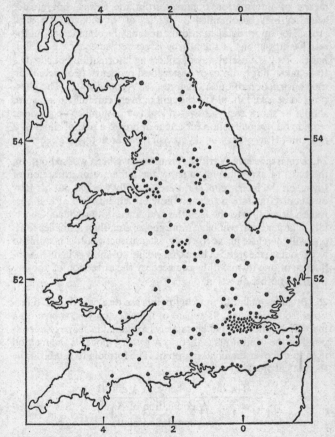

FIG. 73   *Distribution of Marks and Spencer's shops in England and Wales.*

This average depends on the facilities and amenities provided by the centre. The bigger towns will have more and better services and therefore will influence a larger area. The large sphere will be superimposed over and above those of the smaller settlements. Hence there will be a hierarchy of settlements. There may be exceptions to this, as shown above by Harrods and Bentalls.

The boundary lines between the zones may be drawn in by means of information obtained from the towns, but greater accuracy may be obtained by studies of the villages and rural areas. Here more detailed information may be obtained about the relative attractions of the nearby larger settlements. A questionnaire survey is a useful way of collecting information but care has to be taken not to upset or pester local residents. (For details on the construction of questionnaires, *see* Appendix III.) The questions to be asked should be thought out very carefully in advance, should be short, easily answered and few in number—e.g. where would you normally shop for a loaf of bread, a pair of shoes or a new suit? How often would you visit the nearest towns?

24. Urban influence. Various formulae have been worked out, on the basis of experiments, to show the influence or attraction of towns on the intervening rural areas. Reilly worked out his Law of Retail Gravitation to show how settlements will attract customers according to the facilities and amenities provided. Generally, a larger town will have more shops, etc., than a smaller town and will therefore prove to be a greater attraction. It is possible to work out a theoretical breaking-point, to show where the influence of one town will be replaced by the attraction of another town in another direction.

25. Breaking-point. If breaking-points are discovered in all directions from any town, its sphere of influence may be shown on a map. This sphere should be vaguely hexagonal in shape to correspond to the central place theory. A gravity model is the method used to discover the breaking-point. The formula to establish the theoretical breaking-point is:

$$\frac{\text{The distance between A and B}}{1+ \sqrt{\left(\dfrac{\text{Population of A}}{\text{Population of B}}\right)}}$$

In the example of Godalming and Guildford, the relevant figures would be 18,000 (population of Godalming), 56,000 (population of Guildford) and 8 km (the distance between the two towns):

$$\frac{8}{1+\sqrt{\left(\dfrac{56,000}{18,000}\right)}} = 2.89$$

This means that the breaking-point is 2.89 km from Godalming, or 5.11 km from Guildford.

26. Predictions. Another version of the same gravity model idea may be used to show the influences of two nearby larger towns, on a third and smaller settlement. This is an interaction formula and should enable predictions to be made. In the case of Godalming, Guildford and Farnham (population 31,000), it should be possible to forecast, or predict, the relative attractions of Guildford and Farnham to the inhabitants of Godalming. Regarding Godalming as A, Guildford as B, and Farnham as C, the formula required will be:

$$\frac{\text{Population B}}{\text{Population C}} \times \left(\frac{\text{distance from A to C}}{\text{distance from A to B}}\right)^2$$
$$= \frac{56,000}{31,000} \times \left(\frac{13}{8}\right)^2$$
$$= 1.8 \times 2.6$$
$$= 4.68$$

This answer predicts that 4.68 times as many people from Godalming will go to shop in Guildford as compared with the attractions of Farnham. This prediction can be checked by field-work. If the real-life situation does not correspond to the prediction, it will be possible to explain the discrepancy by reference to car-parking facilities, main roads, the attractions of individual shops, etc.

Another formula for the same prediction multiplies the population of two towns and divides by the square of the distance between the towns. The theoretical attractive force of Guildford upon Godalming will be:

$$\frac{56,000 \times 18,000}{8^2}$$

$$= \frac{1,008,000}{64}$$

$$= \quad 15,750$$

The attractive force of Farnham upon Godalming will be:

$$\frac{31,000 \times 18,000}{13^2}$$

$$= \frac{558,000}{169}$$

$$= 3301$$

By dividing 3301 into 15,750 an answer of 4.8 may be obtained, which shows that the attractive force of Guildford is likely to be 4.8 times greater than that of Farnham.

27. Huff's probability model. In an attempt to improve on Reilly's law, Huff devised a formula that enables predictions of shopping habits to be made. The probability is based on the number of shops and the distance from home. The distance can be measured in kilometres or in time. It is assumed that shoppers desiring choice will go to a larger town with a greater number of shops than a smaller, though nearer, town. Therefore distance, together with the degrees of choice, will be the two determinant factors.

If the shopper is confronted with the choice of three towns (Godalming, Guildford, Farnham) it is possible to predict the probability that he, or she, will visit town A (Godalming) rather than town B (Guildford) or town C (Farnham), by using the following formula:

$$\frac{\text{No. of shops in Godalming}}{\text{Distance travelled}} \div \frac{\text{Total no. of shops in 3 towns}}{\text{Total distance}}$$

Taking shoe shops as an example, *Yellow Pages* reveal that Farnham and Godalming each have three, and Guildford eleven. Guildford is 7 km from Godalming and Farnham 13 km. For a shopper living in Godalming and going to shop in Godalming, the distance travelled will be regarded as 1 km and so the formula will be:

$$\frac{3}{1} \div \frac{17}{21} = \frac{3}{1} \times \frac{21}{17} = \frac{63}{17} = 3.71$$

The same formula can be used for the other towns and will give answers as follows:

$$\text{Farnham} \quad \frac{3}{13} \div \frac{17}{21} = \frac{3}{13} \times \frac{21}{17} = \frac{63}{221} = 0.29$$

$$\text{Guildford} \quad \frac{7}{11} \div \frac{17}{21} = \frac{7}{11} \times \frac{21}{17} = \frac{147}{187} = 0.79$$

The three answers 3.71, 0.29, 0.79 give a total of 4.79, so can be converted to (approximately) 77, 6 and 17%. This means there is a 77% probability that shoppers living in Godalming will actually buy shoes in Godalming, but only a 6% probability for visiting Farnham and 17% probability for visiting Guildford.

No account is taken of the size of the shops, or even the reputation, as individual shopkeepers, by their own drive and enthusiasm, may affect the result in real life. Also, the availability of cheap and convenient car-parking facilities may influence the shoppers' choice.

28. Conclusions. Huff, Reilly and others have developed techniques that show the importance of towns on the surrounding countryside and serve to emphasise the significance of regions based on the towns and their spheres of influence. Regional boundaries can be drawn between towns though in reality there would be overlaps, and super-imposed scales of regions. In spite of these difficulties the theoretical regions would provide a model, or a basis, for detailed studies.

PROGRESS TEST 8

1. Define the limits of the urban area nearest to where you live. (1)

2. Compile a land-use map of a nearby area to distinguish the C.B.D. and other zones, if recognisable. (2–7)

3. Obtain figures of rateable values from your local council offices. Construct a map of your town to show the variations in rateable values. Use dark shading for buildings with the highest values and progressively lighter shading for buildings of lower values. (2–3)

4. Draw up a hierarchy of settlements based on population figures for the county or area in which you live. (10)

5. Work out the F.C.V. for five towns in your home area. (11–12)

6. On a 1:50,000 map-tracing, work out the breaking-points for these same five towns and attempt to draw Christaller-type hexagons to show their catchment areas. (13–25)

7. Using the Huff formula, work out the probabilities for three local towns and then test your results by means of a questionnaire field-study. (27 and Appendix III)

CHAPTER IX

Agriculture

LAND-USE VARIATIONS

1. Controlling factors. Agriculture is a world-wide activity and obviously is very varied, both from country to country, and from region to region within a country. For example, agriculture in the south of France is quite different from that of northern England. In northern England the agriculture of the Pennine moorland is quite different from that of lowland Cheshire. The major differences are caused by climate, which provides strict limits that cannot be overcome, except by man-made interference such as glass-houses or irrigation projects. The limits imposed by climate are not normally changeable, however, but within these limits, as for example in England, there are many different farming practices and products. The Fenland area is quite different from the Breckland, in spite of climatic similarities, as the former is very fertile and the latter is naturally infertile. Farming near large towns is often different from that in more isolated areas, even if climatic and soil conditions are similar, because the attractions of a large local market determine what are financially the most rewarding products. In addition to these factors, there are the political influences of government subsidies and personal idiosyncracies. Some farmers like rearing sheep, dairy cattle or beef cattle because they always have done so. Others always produce fruit, or grow wheat or vegetables, in spite of—and not because of—local soil or climatic conditions. Thus many factors help to determine farming.

2. Land-use studies. In order to study or analyse farming, detailed information of land-use is required, together with knowledge of climate, soil types and farming methods, including the importance of fertiliser. Land-use maps on a one-inch scale were compiled in the 1930s and a second survey was completed in the 1960s on a 1:25,000 scale. These maps are a great source of information and are extremely useful, but they are invariably out of date.

Therefore, field-plotting is essential in order to show land-use in any area to be studied. A base map can be constructed on whatever scale is required, but 1:25,000 is often the most suitable, as all fields can be seen, though 1:10,000 is sometimes more useful for work on small areas.

3. Types of survey. Much time is necessary to collect the information required for a complete land-use map. If a large area is being mapped, or if insufficient time is available, there are various techniques for partial surveys. Imagine a town, or a farm, as the centre of the area to be mapped. Line transects can work out like the spokes of a wheel from the hub (which will be the town or farm) to the tyre (which will be the boundary of the region). A minimum of three transects will be necessary and six or eight would guarantee a reasonable coverage of the area, especially near the centre. Transect surveys would enable sectors of land to be mapped, and not merely a narrow strip along the line. Another possibility is to divide the area into a series of squares and select as many squares as it is possible to survey. The squares should be representative of north, south, east and west, both near the middle of the area under consideration, and also near the periphery. Point samples may be used as an alternative method. In order to employ this technique, numbers could be selected in a random fashion, and for this type of sampling, random-number tables would be required (*see* Appendix IV). Sampling along a line, and not at random points, is another technique sometimes used. (Further guidance on sampling is given in III, 2–8.)

Whichever method is employed, an adequate map will be constructed, and this will be the descriptive account of the land-use. An analysis of this information then becomes a possibility, and the land-use can be explained in a logical fashion.

4. Statistics. Detailed statistical information for England and Wales is available from the Ministry of Agriculture Records Office in Guildford, where the records of parish returns are stored. Every parish in England and Wales is included in these records. On a set date each year (1st June), every farmer has to fill in a form to state exactly what is growing in all his fields on that date, and also say exactly how many animals he possesses. Figures 74 and 75 show some of the information that may be obtained from these records.

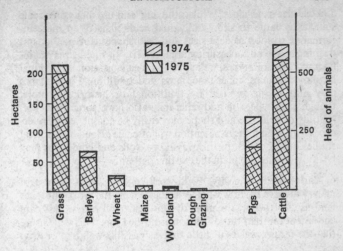

FIG. 74 *The crops and animals grown and reared in Compton Parish, Surrey, 1974–5.*

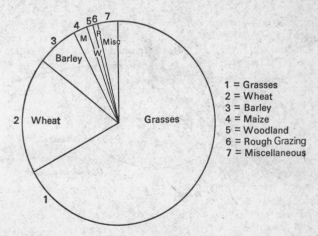

FIG. 75 *Land-use in Compton Parish, 1975 (percentages of total land area).*

5. Field size and shapes. Whilst studying land-use maps on a scale sufficiently large to show individual fields, it is often quite informative to look at field sizes and field shapes (for methods of defining shape and measuring area, *see* III, 9). Field sizes are influenced by soil types, relief, crop, mechanisation, individual farming attitudes, inheritance laws and tradition. Field shapes may also be determined by traditional or historical factors, though crop type, soil and relief may also have some influence. A study of field size and shape may easily be completed by reference to maps, but the explanation will often be helped by practical studies out of doors. In this way crops, soils and landforms may be utilised to help explain the existing pattern.

6. Variations in intensity. Field-work together with the use of maps will serve to show whether distance from the farm influences land-use. In theory, the most distant fields will receive less care and attention than those fields nearest the farm. This will ensure that the farmer wastes as little time as possible walking, or driv-

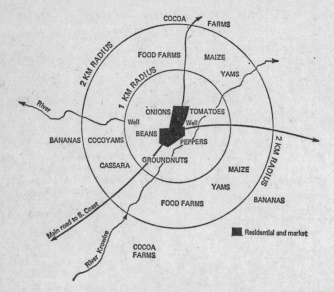

FIG. 76 *Lines of intensity in farming around the village of Agogo in Ghana.*

ing, to the more distant fields. The nearest fields are likely to be used most intensively, for growing vegetables or rearing dairy cattle where daily care and attention are required, whilst the distant fields may be utilised for store cattle or cereals, where only occasional work is necessary. This pattern is not always evident in Britain.

Even in peasant farming communities, where farmers tradition-ally walk many kilometres daily to reach the distant fields, or to utilise many small fragmented strips of land, the fields nearest home are utilised most intensively. This can be clearly seen in southern Italy and Sicily where there is often a vegetable zone around the village, with cereal fields beyond and then an exten-sive pastoral area for goats. This pattern can be seen on the two differing scales of farm and village. Figure 76 shows clearly the three zones visible round the settlement of Agogo in Ghana.

THE FARM MODEL

7. Von Thünen. Johann Heinrich von Thünen wrote about his farm in 1826. On his estate near Rostock, in northern Germany, he worked out a theory of how a land-use pattern should evolve. He assumed a level landscape, uniform soil type, only one form of transport (horse and cart in his day) and only one market. He also worked from the premise that farmers would aim to earn the highest net return possible from each plot of land.

As costs of production would be equal in all areas, the only variable cost would be transport. This cost would rise steadily with increasing distance from the market. As a result, he argued, the crops grown nearest the town would be those which were most perishable or in most frequent demand. These would be the most profitable but, at a set distance from the market, transport costs would become prohibitive, and so an alternative crop would be planted. This crop would be able to bear the greater transport costs and longer transport time.

In the ideal world von Thünen described how on an isotropic plain with a uniform transport system in all directions, circular zones of differing products would appear; his model reflects this (*see* Fig. 77).

In reality the perfect conditions described by von Thünen never appear because of relief and soil variations, and differing forms of communications. What he described was really a model (*see* I, **5**) and thus he provides a very early example of a modern

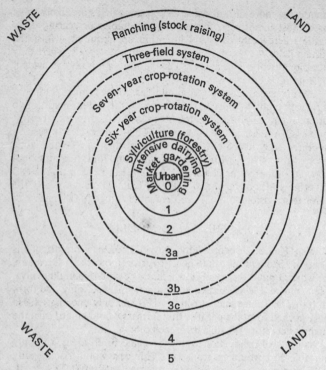

FIG. 77 *Von Thünen's land-use rings.*

technique. This model, in spite of the flaws, is still a very good basis for study. The weaknesses are mainly associated with the facts that uniform soils and relief do not occur widely and transport systems vary and are very different from those near Rostock in the early nineteenth century.

The model shows some resemblance to reality on different scales of study. For example, on large efficient farms there is often more intensive land-use in the zone nearest the farm, with different zones working outwards. The same pattern is evident round towns, with market gardening and dairying often occurring near the suburbs, cereals occurring further afield. The zones do not quite correspond to those outlined by von Thünen, but conditions and times have changed. For instance, the zone of forestry, so important to the wood-burning community of von Thünen's estate, is no longer important in a world of electricity.

8. Economic rent. von Thünen regarded the idea of economic rent as crucial to his views of land-use and the way in which the zone developed. Economic rent is the profit yielded from one field by one crop, over and above the profit any other crop might produce. For example, a field growing potatoes might give a higher profit than if used for sheep rearing. The difference in income would be the economic rent. Figure 78(*a*) shows this idea, which may be applicable to a farm or a village. The horizontal axis portrays distance from the farm but may equally well show distance from the market centre. At a certain point away from the farm, the increased labour costs involved in the production of an intensive crop would reduce its profitability, and the more extensive type of farming would become more profitable (*see* Fig.

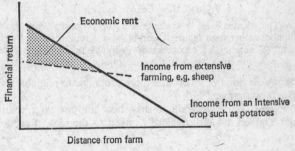

(a)

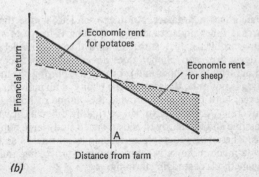

(b)

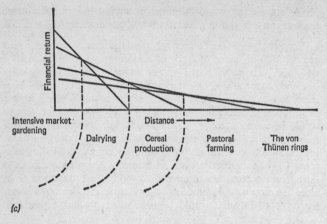

(c)

FIG. 78   *Economic rent.*

(*a*) The shaded area represents the higher profit from growing potatoes rather than rearing sheep up to a certain distance from the farm; (*b*) at point A it becomes more profitable to rear sheep; (*c*) land-use rings based on the concept of economic rent.

78(*b*)). At point A it becomes more profitable to rear sheep than to grow potatoes.

Figure 78(*c*) endeavours to show how land-use rings, as in the von Thünen model, are closely linked to the idea of economic rent.

FARMING PROBLEMS

9. Simulations and games. Another useful technique that helps towards a fuller understanding of farming is to try to simulate farming problems. Just as the use of a theory or model such as that devised by von Thünen does not provide a perfect explanation of farming methods and productivity, playing a game about farming is not quite the same as the reality of an individual farm; however, both these ideas provide the outline of how all farms will operate. As every farm will be slightly different, it would be impossible and foolhardy to endeavour to study large numbers of farms. These two geographical techniques of models and games provide much more satisfactory, thought-provoking and stimulating methods of studying farming.

Many games have been devised in order to help understand farming and farming problems. All have to consider the variables of climate, prices, yields and also the slow rate of change in the way that animal herds or tree crops take years to build up, and how even field crops cannot be changed in less than a year.

Two possible ideas for the basis of games that may be devised by any students are given below.

10. Farm game A. Start with 100 units, which may be utilised in any way the player wishes. Units are calculated as follows: one hectare of crop-land $= 2$ units; one large animal $= 1$ unit; one sheep $= \frac{1}{3}$ unit; one pig $= \frac{1}{5}$ unit; and one chicken $= \frac{1}{100}$ unit. Each player can select any arrangement of crops and animals (up to the starting allocation of 100 units). Looking after each crop would demand different hours of work, as on the following scale (using man-days of 8 hours work per day):

Dairy cattle   50
Wheat   2 (unless the combine-harvester broke down)

and so on. This would enable labour requirements to be estimated. It would also outline problems, e.g. do you wish to rear dairy cattle or grow vegetables, thereby earning high returns per hectare, but necessitating employing labour? Or grow crops yielding less per hectare, but being able to manage without hired assistance? A scale of returns per hectare is also necessary before the game may be played.

Having decided on the contents of the farm, scale of labour required, scale of returns per hectare, etc., each player in the game is ready to start.

Assess how many units each player would have scored in order to discover the most successful farmer.

Different situations can be introduced by throwing a dice to discover weather conditions, or by drawing cards for good or bad additions to the farming. Cards could be made to give fertile alluvial soil in one field, or a new variety of seeds giving a higher yield, or a higher market price than expected.

11. Farm game B. There is a farm of 10 fields each with a known area:

Field 1: Orchard.
Field 2: Permanent pasture.
Field 3: Sown grass.

Fields 4–10: Changeable—using crops decided on at the start of the game.

Each crop is known to yield differently, in differing climatic conditions. There are six possible weather situations (using a dice), or it is possible to use twenty or so weather situations, using cards to draw for the weather.

12. Sample studies. The study of farms in general terms is better than attempting to study a vast number of specific individual farms. However, a close look at an individual farm will help to show its uniqueness, though, when compared to others, it will emphasise some common characteristics. It is worth visiting a farm to learn:

(*a*) how the farmer decides which crops to plant or which animals to rear;

(*b*) how much fertiliser is required;

(*c*) the crop rotation;

(*d*) variations in fields;

(*e*) transport facilities for marketing the products; and

(*f*) how much labour and machinery are available, etc.

PROGRESS TEST 9

1. What are the major factors that will influence the type of farming practised by any farmer? (**1**)

2. How would you set about collecting agricultural land-use information for a parish or any rural area? (**2–4**)

3. How would you test the hypothesis that the choice of crop or animal is determined by size, shape and location of the field under consideration? (**5–6**)

4. Describe how the von Thünen model may be relevant to any area in England. (**7–8**)

5. Make a study of a farm near to your home, and draw a map (1:25,000 or 1:10,000) to show all the fields and their contents on any one particular day. If possible, compare the same fields with what was in them twelve months previously.

CHAPTER X

Population Geography

INTRODUCTION

1. Human studies. Man's role in geographical studies has become more and more important as he has spread his influence over the land, changing the shape of his environment to suit his own needs. The study of this influence in the form of human geography developed during the Industrial Revolution, when man became a determining factor in the land's shape as he increased in abundancy.

Human and social studies are very broad and indeterminate subjects designed to cover an incredibly wide spectrum of information. They have become overlooked in school geography, particularly since the trend has been away from "regional" geography, turning more in favour of the "systematic" approach that gives little scope for studying human variations in detail.

Recently, however, interest has been stirred up by the debate on man's future and his dubious control of the environment. This has become the basis of much controversy and as a result population geography has been stimulated by many research projects. There is consequently an increase in the literature on this subject.

2. Spatial studies. Population geography is concerned with demonstrating how spatial variations in the distribution, composition and growth of population are related to the nature of places. There are qualitative studies in abundance but it is only recently that rather more detailed and sophisticated quantification has been carried out.

A close correlation to the behaviour of plants and animals has led biogeographical theory (*see* VI,1) to be applied to explain man's social and economic tendencies.

3. The problems of information and information collection. Geographers are faced with vast amounts of information about population from all over the world and have to deal with a great variety and varying quality of information made available from a wide range of sources. The quality of information provided by the developed western nations is generally good and reliable, making population studies reliable. On the other hand, Communist countries are not liberal with their information and even the number of victims of earthquakes in China in 1976 was estimated rather than accurately reported in the world press. Underdeveloped countries may have some reliable sources but generally a lack of coverage and communications make for incomplete data.

The gathering and analysis of world statistics is almost a hopeless task, but efforts have been made to centralise data, particularly by the United Nations Organisation, which publishes year books of some reliability that are invaluable in geographical research.

SURVEYS

4. Official surveys. The census is probably the best known official survey in Great Britain and was first carried out in 1801. It is held every ten years, with a 10% sample survey at five-yearly intervals (but *see* III, 8). A great variety of questions are asked, designed to give information on the individual, abode and occupation. The census has to be filled in correctly, and failure to do so is a criminal offence. Tremendous problems occur, however, particularly those of illiteracy, evasion and misunderstandings.

Parochial records are generally reliable, giving information on the electorate, births, marriages and deaths. Tax returns provide a sound record of earnings and related data, but even these cannot be considered totally reliable, since evasion and "tax fiddling" occur.

Migrants are the major cause for concern, since both immigrants and emigrants are difficult to locate. Some information is gained on fairly stable members of the community. However, roving members are less likely to be counted.

5. Unofficial surveys. The student can gather much information by devising his own questionnaire that, if composed carefully, will bring forth a wealth of data (*see* Appendix III). Sampling has to be done, as a questionnaire is a time-consuming process. Questions should be brief, simple to understand, and not too personal. The man in the street will say "no" rather than "yes" to a student who is prying too much.

Information on people's behaviour can be gained from shopping habits, occupations, journeys made and entertainments. Personal surveys can reveal information on these, but it is also possible to go straight to the shop or the employment agency, for example, in order to discover more about a sample population.

6. Some other sources of population data.

(a) World Health Organisation.

(b) Registrar-General's Office.

(c) Ministry offices.

(d) Office of Population Censuses and Surveys.

(e) International Labour Office.

(f) UNESCO Statistical Year Book.

(g) Annual Estimates of Population (H.M.S.O.).

POPULATION MEASUREMENTS

7. **Inputs to the population.** There are two ways a population can increase: by child-birth and immigration.

(a) *Births.* Before discussing the various ways births can be measured, it is necessary to clarify some terms connected with child-births: *fertility* refers to the actual occurrence of births in a specific population; *fecundity* is the reproductive capacity of a population; and *reproduction* is the replacement of individuals by the birth of others.

Measurements used for child-birth include the following:

(i) Birth-rates, which measure the number of births proportionate to the population as a whole. Crude birth-rates are the ratio of the number of live births in a period of time to the total population, invariably multiplied by 1,000 or 100.

(ii) Fertility ratios,

$$\frac{\text{Number of children under 5}}{\text{Number of women 15–44}} \times 100$$

The significance of the age-range 15–44 is that these are normally the child-bearing years.

(iii) Age-specific birth-rate,

$$100 \times \frac{\text{Number of births to mother (or father) at age } x}{\text{Number of women (or men) at age } x}$$

(b) *In-migration*. Immigration rates are given generally as annual values showing:

    (i) places of origin,

    (ii) destination,

    (iii) occupation, and

    (iv) reasons for movement.

8. Outputs from the population. As with input to the population, there are two factors affecting the decline in a population's number: deaths and emigration.

(a) *Deaths*. There are numerous measurements that can be made of the deaths occurring in a population:

(i) Deaths as a result of child-birth and in infancy can reveal a great deal about medicinal development within a population: comparisons can be made between still births and live births; a count can be made of infant mortality (young humans are the most vulnerable to disease); and the maternal mortality-rate can be worked as occurrence of this type of death per 1,000 of population within a specific age-group.

(ii) The average age at which death occurs can be expressed as life-expectancy or longevity.

(iii) The crude death-rate can be calculated as the number of deaths per 1,000 of the population, the age-specific death-rate being calculated in the same way as the age-specific birth-rate above.

Survival tables and curves can be drawn (*see* **17** below) to depict the numbers of live people in each age group (or cohort, starting with a population for a particular cohort say 0–4 years old in 1975), and noting the losses made within that cohort after each year.

(b) *Out-migration*. Similar measures are employed for emigration and of course the loss of skilled workers ("brain-drain") will deprive the country or place of origin, but may benefit the receptive country. Distance moved is a very important measure since the distance may give a clue to the reason for migration and whether or not it is to be a permanent or temporary move. The present ease of migration within Commonwealth countries has contributed to the large numbers of Australians in London. Similarly, the new situation within the E.E.C. has speeded up the growing movement between countries in the Market, particularly in the form of "guest-workers".

9. Other measurements. Other measurements that can be made of a population include:

    (*a*) marriage rate per 1,000 people in a population;
    (*b*) age of marriage;
    (*c*) divorce rates;
    (*d*) size of family;
    (*e*) sex composition within the population;
    (*f*) age structure of the population;

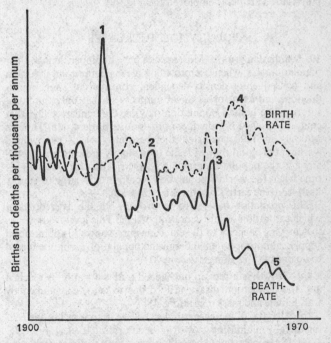

    1 Volcanic eruption
    2 Influenza epidemic
    3 Hurricanes, polio and poor economy
    4 Post — war baby boom
    5 Improvement in medicine

FIG. 79 *Causes of population change.*

(g) employment data and socio-economic groupings;

(h) nationality, language and religion.

There are many variables involved in studying populations. The measurements noted above are just a few of the obvious indices that help explain the structure of a population. The demographer has to draw this information together and account for population change. With this tremendous amount of information it is no wonder that quantitative techniques and population computerisation are being employed (*see* Fig. 79).

POPULATION INCREASES

10. Malthusian growth. Most species have an upper limit to their population size, when overcrowding means famine and irritation and consequently density-dependent controls cut short reproduction, and even forces down numbers so that only the fittest survive. The human population may have a similar ceiling that could be reached if growth continues at its present rate. Thomas Malthus in 1798 predicted the possibility of over-crowding, warning the world that with the food supply growing arithmetically and the population growing geometrically, there would be a time when the world's population would be too large to supply itself from the earth's resources (*see* Fig. 80).

This prediction has yet to be proved, but the fixed point at which saturation occurs is not impossible. This level is known as the carrying capacity of the environment. Above this point, food supply cannot meet demand and the population would be forced to do one of three things (*see* Fig. 81):

(a) Growth can remain unchanged until saturation is reached and the population disastrously drops to zero, encouraged by war, famine and mass migration. (I)

(b) The rate of increase can decrease as it approaches the ceiling thereby minimising growth at the saturation level. (II)

(c) It can overshoot the ceiling from time to time, oscillating about the ceiling, depending on food availability. (III)

11. Checks on Malthusian growth. Famine is caused by unusual weather conditions or some other disaster, such as pests or soil erosion. The worst hit areas are the marginal areas—for example, the Sahel or Bangladesh, where the slightest fluctuation from regular conditions can cause poor harvests and poor food supply.

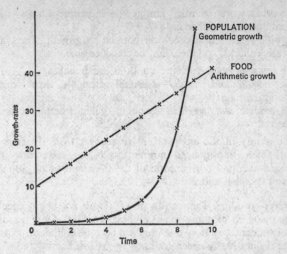

FIG. 80 *Geometric population-growth and arithmetic increase in food supply.*

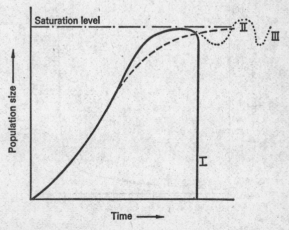

FIG. 81 *Effects on population of its meeting the saturation level.*

The world's worst recorded famine was in eastern China—with nine million people killed in 1877–9.

Famine is a natural check on population growth. There are other such checks, and these may be classified as:

(*a*) *non-recurrent*—volcanic eruptions, earthquakes;

(*b*) *periodic and regular*—seasonal droughts, low winter temperatures;

(*c*) *periodic and irregular*—flooding, gales, freezing temperatures.

The ability of the environment to recover from disasters is remarkable. Man-induced atomic explosions have not discouraged eventual regeneration of the flora and fauna populations on Pacific islands.

12. Over-crowding. The world's population is not homogeneous but is made up of many creeds and classes. Over-dense populations experience friction, and conflicts become abundant. Losses of life do not really check Malthusian growth, merely reducing numbers for short periods of time—say, a generation. The Second World War, for example, claimed 7.3 million lives, and the U.S. Civil War 5.8 million, but all regions involved have eventually

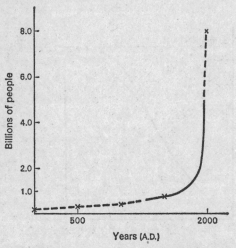

FIG. 82 *World population growth.*

replaced their lost numbers and regained a balanced population. Britain and Sweden are now nearing a negative growth rate.

The future may see a more positive check on a nation's growth (something on the scale of the Jewish suffering in the Second World War) for nuclear war is the greatest threat to the human race in terms of international conflict. With two competing nations there can only be one survivor.

13. The world's population. The world's population now stands at approximately 4.0 billion. In 1800 some 906 million lived on the Earth; in 1900, 1,608 million; and in 1950, 2,407 million (2.4 billion). With this rate of growth, by 2000 the population could be 6.0 billion (*see* Fig. 82).

Population increase can come about by a rise in the percentage reproductive rate, death-rates remaining constant, or by a decline in the death-rate (through improved medicine) and a constant reproductive rate. Table VIII shows that birth-rates and death-rates (per 1,000) have generally been declining.

TABLE VIII: BIRTH AND DEATH-RATES, 1861–1974

	Great Britain		India		Japan	
	Birth	Death	Birth	Death	Birth	Death
1861–5	35.1	22.5	—	—	—	—
1901–5	28.3	16.2	—	—	—	—
1921–5	20.3	12.3	—	—	—	—
1941–5	16.1	12.9	31.4	20.7	29.5	16.5
1946–50	18.2	11.9	—	—	—	—
1948	—	—	25.4	16.0	—	—
1950	—	—	—	—	28.3	10.9
1974	13.3	12.2	17.0	7.4	42.0	14.6

Gaps in the table indicate years for which no information is available.

Estimates show that the world's growth-rate is about two per cent per year. By projecting this back in time, the population of the world would reduce to one person by 500 B.C. We know that man has been on the earth since 500,000 B.C. It is possible that the population growth-rate has not been steady throughout history, but was much slower in the initial stages.

EXPONENTIAL GROWTH

14. An exponential growth model. Consider a living organism, for example the mallard or wild duck, living on an isolated island in the spring of 1972. There is an imaginary population of ten (five males/five females). During each breeding season (spring), a pair produces ten offspring, always five male and five female. After each year the parents birds die, before the next breeding season. There is no migration. -

One can lay criticism on the generalisations made, but this model is designed to show exponential growth and give some clue to how a population might grow under ideal circumstances.

Table IX shows how the growth occurs.

TABLE IX: EXPONENTIAL GROWTH OF A POPULATION
OF MALLARDS

Years	Population numbers	Pairs	Offspring	Winter deaths	Population next spring
1972	10	5	50	10	50
1973	50	25	250	50	250
1974	250	125	1,250	250	1,250
1975	1,250	625	6,250	1,250	6,250
1976	6,250	3,125	31,250	6,250	31,250
1977	31,250	15,625	156,250	15,625	156,250
1978	156,250	78,125	781,250	78,125	781,250

The curve described (*see* Fig. 83) shows an exponential growth, a simplified situation in which growth or decline in the population is unchecked by homeostatic mechanisms (*see* VI, **3**), and the rate of change is proportional to the level reached.

$$\frac{d(N)}{dt} = rN$$

where N = number of individuals
r = rate of natural increase

$\frac{d(\ )}{dt}$ = rate of change, i.e. change per unit of time

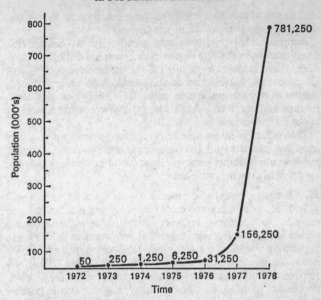

FIG. 83 *Exponential growth in the population of mallards.*

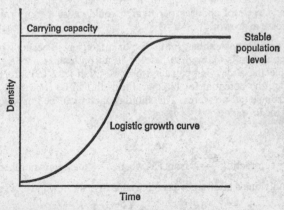

FIG. 84 *Logistic (S-shaped) population growth.*

the amount of growth is related to the population. As the population grows, so the rate of change is greater.

Applying this model to human populations, we can see how small changes in the rate of natural increase are critical. Populations grow rapidly, especially in the under-developed world. Consequently, natural checks are less likely to occur, allowing continued growth until eventually the environmental limit is reached and surpassed. At this stage, over-crowding may bring about disastrous results.

This situation might appear rather too generalised to worry man. But man can only behave as an animal; this rate of growth is not an impossibility—the warnings must be taken seriously and exponential growth controlled.

15. Checks to exponential growth. As the threat of exponential growth becomes more and more obvious, there is a need to limit growth. As resources become exhausted and over-crowding makes life uncomfortable, there will be a need to achieve zero population growth. To achieve this, replacement reproduction is necessary, implying 2.3 children per married couple. Two children replace their parents (eventually) and the 0.3 is to cover people not married, or who do not reproduce. This is possible through greater demographic education and contraception. However, the world's demographic problems would not be solved immediately. Momentum from present growth would still cause the world's population to swell two to five times by A.D. 2000. Only lower targets of children per family would cause a more rapid decrease in growth.

16. Logistic population growth. Exponential growth occurs when a population is allowed to develop in an optimal environment. By placing a carrying capacity, or saturation level (S) into the model, the potential for biological growth will be controlled by environmental pressures. This limiting factor can be introduced into the formula:

$$\frac{d(N)}{dt} = rN$$

By subtracting $\frac{S-N}{S}$ from rN, where $S =$ maximum number of individuals allowed by carrying capacity, we now have:

$$\frac{d(N)}{dt} = rN - \left(\frac{S-N}{S}\right)$$

A modified curve is thus developed and this is known as the logistic curve, shaped characteristically as an S (*see* Fig. 84).

OTHER POPULATION MEASUREMENTS

17. Survivorship curves. We are not just concerned with the numbers of people, but also have an interest in the sex and age structure of populations to give some clue as to how populations will develop. A survivorship curve will show the structure of a population at any one point in time. By placing more than one curve on the graph (i.e. a multi-function graph) different populations can be compared. For example, developed nations will be portrayed in a different shape from undeveloped nations. It is possible to follow one particular age group of people through their life history until death (*see* Fig. 85).

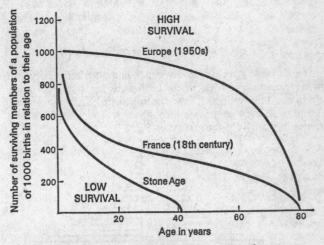

FIG. 85 *Multi-function graph showing survivorship curves.*

18. Population pyramids. By displaying the sex, age and number of people in the form of a bar graph, a population pyramid is produced. From these a vast amount of information is available and varying stages of development within a particular population may be explained.

The following examples show the type of information that can be extracted:

(*a*) *Stable population.* These are typical of European countries, practising birth control. There is a well-balanced structure throughout all age groups. Males and females are of comparable proportions (although more females tend to survive into old age), without a huge amount of dependent individuals. The very young and old are not swamping the population (*see* Fig. 86).

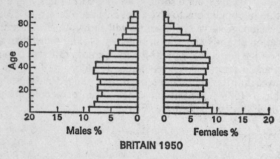

FIG. 86 *Age–sex pyramid of a stable population.*

(*b*) *Expanding population.* An expanding population is typical of developing countries, where birth rates are high but recent medicinal improvements have controlled high infant-mortality. There is an even death-rate throughout the population, with a noticeably small old-age group (*see* Fig. 87).

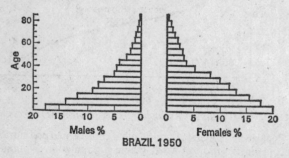

FIG. 87 *Age–sex pyramid of an expanding population.*

(*c*) *Contracting population.* These are found in over-developed or stable countries where low birth-rates and death-rates suggest much birth control and high degrees of medicinal skill. A large number of aged people will put pressure on the working population. The size of the population is declining and the average age is becoming higher (*see* Fig. 88).

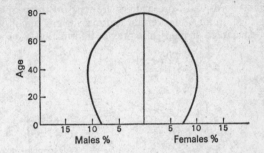

FIG. 88   *Age–sex graph of a contracting population.*

(*d*) *Two anomalies.* Figure 89 shows an age pyramid with high immigration, particularly in the male sector, and an example of high war-losses. The casualties were mainly young men.

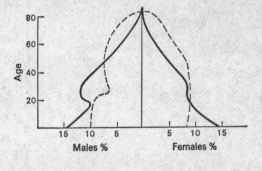

FIG. 89   *Age–sex graph showing the influences of immigration and war.*

POPULATION MOVEMENTS

19. Place names. A careful study of place names on maps may be informative to the geographer in tracing population movements. Different words and word endings are relics of the people who first settled an area, and certain features such as tumuli, which are often marked on maps, also provide information (*see* Fig. 90).

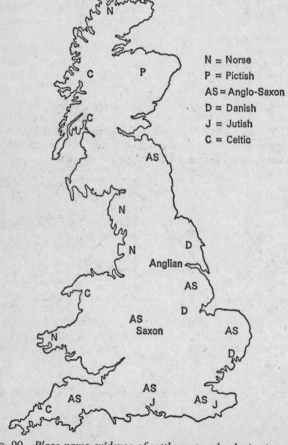

N = Norse
P = Pictish
AS = Anglo-Saxon
D = Danish
J = Jutish
C = Celtic

FIG. 90   *Place name evidence of settlement and colonisation.*

(a) Celtic names include: *aber* (river mouth); *caer* (fortress); *pen* (hill); *porth* (harbour); and *tre* (hamlet).

(b) Roman names include: *caster* or *cester* (fort or camp); and *port* (a gateway).

(c) Anglo-Saxon names include: *-ing* and *-ham* (homestead); *-ton* (enclosure, town); *-mere* (lake); *-stead* (place); *-ley* (clearing); and *holt* (wood).

(d) Scandinavian names include: *beck* (stream); *booth* (summer pasture); *-by* (village); *gill* (valley or ravine); *kirk* (church); *thorpe* (hamlet); *fell* (hill or mountain); and *tarn* (lake).

20. Map evidence. A study of an area such as Lincolnshire or Norfolk will reveal the influence of different waves of settlers. It is a worthwhile and interesting exercise to plot the word-endings of settlements along a line across England. Studies of O.S. maps 122 (Skegness), 121 (Lincoln), and 120 (Mansfield) will show the gradual decrease of Scandinavian names, until Anglo-Saxon word-endings predominate. The west coast of England in that latitude (sheet 117, Chester) will show a sprinkling of Norse endings.

Another interesting exercise is to plot word-endings in the Weald to establish waves of settlements. The first settlers avoided the wet clay areas and *-ing, -ham, -ton, -tun* (an earlier form of *-ton*) are common endings on the chalk and sandstone ridges. Later settlements had to clear woodland or drain wet areas, and *-ley, -den* or *-croft* are some of the word-endings that appear.

DIFFUSION

21. Spatial diffusion. The movement of people and animals is a major part of the geographer's study, but there is much more information to be obtained from motion studies, in the form of reasons for migration, decision-making and environmental perception. Spatial studies look to explain in greater detail the patterns of geographical movements.

Colonisation, for example, the opening up of North America, tends to follow ordered patterns, though human irrationality often causes deviations in otherwise logical flows. The choice of the easiest path, the cheapest mode of transport and the safest routes created distinct paths across the U.S.A. and Canada. However, some of the routes are less rational.

Far more rapid and more sweeping is the spread of culture that is the result of human movement; the spread of Christianity, for example, which used man as its messenger, diffused from the Holy Lands. The motion is rather like the spread of ripples from a splash of a pebble in a millpond. Diffusion waves move outward almost for an infinite length of time. However, physical barriers or isolation will sometimes prevent further movement.

Some diffusion waves are concentrated down channels of least resistance (e.g. transport routes) and, of course, some waves have more strength and consequently cause faster, more complete changes than others.

It is not, then, just the movement of people that concerns the geographer, but the innovations that go with them. Ideas are now more easily spread with the power of telecommunications, and diffusion occurs in a more sophisticated manner. However, despite the change in speed of the movement, the principle is the same.

22. Types of diffusion. There are three types of diffusion:

(a) *Expanding diffusion.* The originating idea remains central and the idea spreads out from person to person rather like the pebble in the millpond. News bulletins from Broadcasting House are typical of this form. Contagious diseases are also good examples, as are hierarchical diffusions, where ideas are passed down or up through the classes.

(b) *Relocation diffusion.* Here the originating force moves from one region to another. A carrier of a contagious disease may create this kind of diffusion where the disease is left in one area. After he moves on, the disease is eventually cured, but the carrier has already taken his disease to new receptive areas. Fashions often reach rural areas in England a long time after they have become out of fashion in the towns.

(c) These two types of diffusion often combine, to form the third type.

23. A model of diffusion. A diffusion model is an example of how diffusion can be used to explain past movements or predict the future development and spread of ideas. The model was devised in Sweden by Torsten Hagerstrand, who involved the probability theory in the process of diffusion.

The probability or chance that an idea will spread depends mainly on distance. This can be measured as an actual interval between two individuals or in the form of a hierarchy, where information is only passed through adjacent steps and not in a jumping fashion.

The basic assumption is that the probability of contact between two individuals will become weaker the further they are apart. The relationship has an inverse proportion and appears to be exponential in shape.

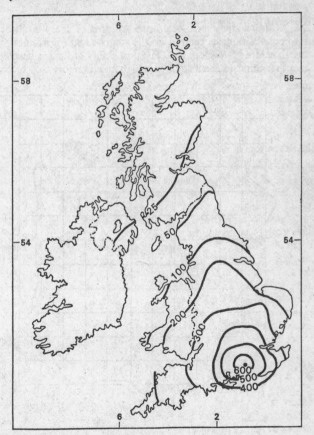

FIG. 91 *Isopleth map of numbers of telephone calls made per annum from a school.*

This idea may be tested by counting the number of telephone calls made from an office or school. The fall off should be exponential with a higher number of short distance calls and fewer trunk or overseas calls.

By plotting these figures on a map and joining areas receiving equal attention from the source area, a trend-surface map or isopleth map can be drawn to show regional trends of contact (*see* Fig. 91).

24. Diffusion study of a local area. An area of study is divided into equal size grids centred on the source area, for example an urban centre of development. The probability of further development reaching adjacent squares is high and therefore they receive

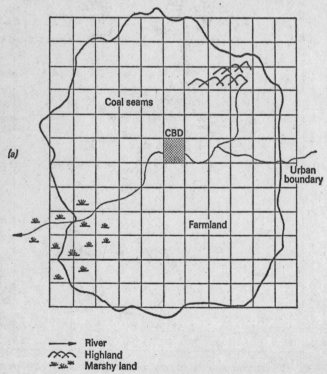

FIG. 92(*a*)

high probability values. The further afield one moves from that point, the smaller is the probability of contact. The whole area likely to be influenced by urban development—say, a municipal borough—should have total probability values equal to 100%, i.e. there is no chance of sampling a square outside the area of study (*see* Fig. 92(*a*) and (*b*)).

To make this operational, the probability values are converted into a series of numbers totalling, in this case, 10,000 digits. The N.W. grid square will represent digits 0–95 rather than just a pro-

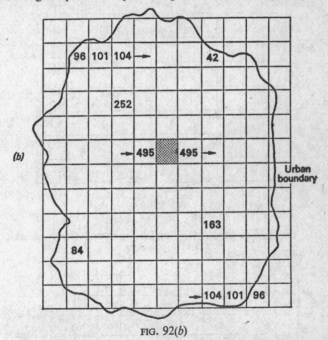

FIG. 92(*b*)

bability 0.0096. The S.E. grid becomes 9903–9999 digits instead of probability value 0.0096 (*see* Fig. 92(*c*)).

Using a random-number table (*see* Appendix IV), numbers are selected and these will provide the path along which the information will be passed. Obviously the squares near the source will have a high number of digits and will have a high chance of being "hit" as the random number is drawn.

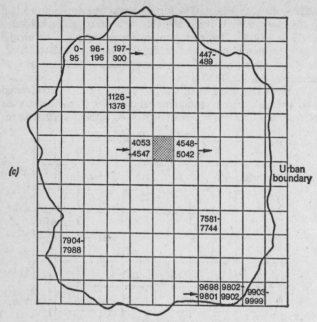

FIG. 92(c)
Diffusion study of an area.

(a) Urban grid overlay; (b) some probability values; (c) grids allocated
random numbers.

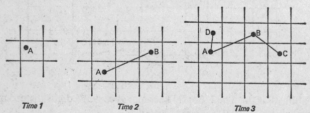

FIG. 93 *Spatial diffusion.*

Time 1: source-cell A holds information; time 2: first message trans-
mitted to randomly-chosen cell B; time 3: message reaches cells C and
D. The process of choosing random cells continues until the whole grid
has received the message.

The procedure is best shown in diagram form (*see* Fig. 93). It should be noted that there are many basic and limiting assumptions made for this model to work, but more sophisticated adaptations have been made to accommodate real-world conditions. These are, however, rather out of our reach.

Application of this technique has been used in urban studies to show how urban sprawl coincides with planners' predictions and physical conditions. Urban development is not always rational and the deviations between the observed and expected occurrences have to be explained.

HUMAN AWARENESS

25. Perception studies. Man continually perceives his environment and makes a stock of information related to his personal needs. This forms a basis for decision-making. If there was no input of fresh information or experience of events then the perceived environment would cease to change.

Communication and innovation are so rapid that this is unlikely to occur. However, isolated, primitive peoples may have this steady state assuming they remain uninfluenced by outside forces.

The perception of hazards has stimulated interest in demographers, climatologists and economists. Man in an unstable area can only assess the site of his settlement in terms of the probability that a flood, cyclone or similar natural disaster might occur. There are risks to be taken.

26. Game theory. In attempting to develop pioneer regions, for example, there was often a risk, decisions being based on minimal information. The process of settlement took the form of a gamble or probabilistic game and recent attempts to simulate this have been based on a branch of mathematics called game theory. Straightforward gaming in classrooms simulates the problems faced and decisions made in the real world. They are designed to incorporate experiences faced by designers, planners and entrepreneurs.

Individuals tend to be over-optimistic and become risk-takers to satisfy their own needs. The Tennessee Valley farmers took risks and lost, as did the Sahel peasants. In areas such as the Sahel risks are far greater, but people who have lived under this danger for centuries are hard to move. They have been brought up challenging the environment and do not respond kindly to "Western development". Disastrous years are soon forgotten and the individuals carry on their task for survival.

Perception studies are a valuable means of obtaining information about the local environment and may be applied to many geographical studies.

PROGRESS TEST 10

1. What problems might be encountered in attempting a population survey in a shanty town? (1–6)

2. Discuss the relationship between population growth in a developing country and migration patterns into and out of the country. Which factor might cause inaccurate results? (7–16)

3. Explain the difference between exponential and logistic population growth. (14, 16)

4. What is spatial diffusion? What factors can limit or increase the spread of ideas throughout a country or region? (21–24)

5. Why might a peasant farmer in an arid region stay on after a series of droughts, even though his crops have repeatedly failed? (25, 26)

CHAPTER XI

Transport

NETWORKS

1. Introduction. Transport systems range from the pack animal and dug-out canoe in sparsely populated and under-developed areas, to motorways, high-speed trains and aircraft. Many routes are merely single tracks, without any side-roads or junctions, but as routes increase, transport networks develop. The growth of networks, as of all transport links, is influenced by physical factors, notably relief, but true networks will only really be developed in areas that have some economic development and a fairly high standard of living.

2. Network analysis. A network is a set of lines (routes) that join or cross each other at junctions. Description of networks may not be easy if they are complex. Analysis will obviously be more difficult. Therefore, techniques have been developed for network analysis and examples of these will be demonstrated below. These methods or techniques are very useful but they are only a means to an end, and not the end in themselves.

Network analysis will often simplify existing patterns and, therefore, it is not a perfect method and renders itself open to criticism. However, the analysis will measure the pattern quantitatively, which is a great recommendation, and will enable precise comments to be made. Comparisons between networks may also be made with precision and confidence. The study of a network will also help to explain how, why and where the routeways evolved.

3. Density of communications. The density of communications will vary over a continent. For example, in South America:

(a) Complex networks appear in Sao Paulo State of Brazil and on the Pampas, though these would not compare with the networks of the Ruhr, Greater London or Merseyside and Greater Manchester. Here is yet another example of the influence, effect and problem of scale, when studying geographical phenomena.

(b) Areas with a few lines may be found surrounding the networks mentioned, and also in central Chile, north-east Brazil and parts of Venezuela and Colombia.

(c) Single routeways occur in parts of the Andes, Patagonia and elsewhere.

(d) Large expanses of Amazonas, the Andes and Atacama contain no routes. This is because of the lack of population and lack of economic development, and, in the case of Amazonas, the availability of waterways, a better form of transport in this area.

Even in continents that are densely populated, with vast systems of complex networks, there are areas to correspond with (d) above, i.e. no routes. These occur in parts of the Alps and in the Highlands of Scotland. Hence, any technique suitable for one part of the world will probably be useful elsewhere.

4. Network measurements. The area enclosed within a network is called the inside region, the rest of the area to be studied the outside region.The diameter of a network is not the same as an ordinary mathematical diameter. It may be discovered by counting the number of edges (or links, *see* II, 8) in the shortest path between the two extreme or most distant points in the network.

The actual limits of the area under consideration should also be assessed in a mathematical fashion. The measurement of a peripheral line drawn round the outermost points is one system, or a fixed diameter circle may also be used. The diameter may encircle the outermost points or may remain entirely within the innermost lines of the network. There are also techniques used specifically for measuring the size of the shape (*see* III, 9).

CONNECTIVITY

5. Beta index. The beta index is a useful method for making quantified comparisons of connectivity. The final result is less than one if the network has poor links, is exactly one if there is a single circuit, and is more than one if the network is complex and contains more than one circuit. The beta index is achieved by dividing the number of nodes (or junctions, *see* II, 8) into the number of edges: $B = E/V$. This shows connectivity but not distance. In Fig. 95 the beta index is $\frac{7}{6}$ or 1.16.

6. Matrices. A matrix is a layout of numbers in columns and rows. Each number in the matrix is known as an element or cell, and is identified by the column and row number where it occurs. Figure 94 is an example of a matrix.

Hence, number 10 in the third row and third column is 10_{33}. Matrices can also consist of binary numbers, 0 and 1, so that if the element 10 in the matrix in Fig. 94 had been 0, it would be identified as 0_{33}.

Binary numbers are useful to show the presence (1) or absence (0) of a feature being quantified. They are often used to indicate connectivity in a network.

7. Network matrices. Using a binary matrix to show the connectivity in Fig. 95, a direct link between nodes is recorded as 1, and if there is no direct link an 0 is written in the matrix. Five nodes is the minimum number to be worthy of consideration, and our example uses six. A node cannot connect to itself and this explains the diagonal line of dashes in the matrix in Fig. 96.

It is interesting to compare the existing number of routes with the maximum number possible. The formula to establish maximum connectivity is n (the number of points) minus 1 (because one point cannot connect to itself). On a matrix the maximum number of elements $= n^2 - n$. In transport networks, all flows can be reversed and this number has to be halved to give $(n^2 - n)$. The actual number of links divided by the maximum connectivity will give an answer ranging from 0 (no interconnectivity) to 1 (where the actual number $=$ maximum possible). Quantitative studies of connectivity will enable a well-developed, populated area to be compared with a rural, sparsely populated area in a precise fashion, and not simply by saying that one area has many more routes than another.

8. Cyclomatic numbers. There are other measures of connectivity in addition to the beta index and matrices. In order to find the cyclomatic number of the network, it is necessary to count the number of edges, add one to this total, and then subtract the number of nodes. This gives the following formula:

$$e - n + 1 \text{ (where } e = \text{edges, } n = \text{nodes)}$$

Using this method, all simple networks will have a value of 0, and therefore for these cases, the beta index is much more suitable.

9. The alpha index. The alpha index makes full use of cyclomatic numbers, and is a better measure of complex networks than the beta index. It gives the cyclomatic number expressed as a fraction

Columns

6	8	11	3	9	2
4	7	6	1	2	9
8	11	10	6	4	5
3	7	8	5	3	1
10	8	6	5	3	8

Rows

FIG. 94   *A matrix.*

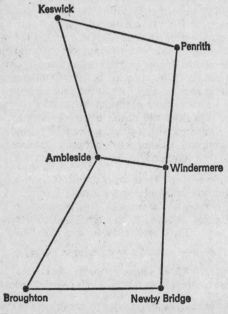

FIG. 95   *Topological map of a network of roads in part of the Lake District.*

		A	B	C	D	E	F	
Keswick	A	–	1	1	0	0	0	2
Penrith	B	1	–	0	1	0	0	2
Ambleside	C	1	0	–	1	1	0	3
Windermere	D	0	1	1	–	0	1	3
Broughton	E	0	0	1	0	–	1	2
Newby Bridge	F	0	0	0	1	1	–	2

FIG. 96 *A binary matrix to show the connectivity of the network in Fig. 95.*

of the maximum possible cyclomatic number for a particular network. The formula for working out alpha indices is:

$e-n+1$ (this is the cyclomatic number)

$2n-5$ (this is the maximum possible value of a cyclomatic number)

The index is obtained by careful use of this formula, but if a percentage answer is required, the figure obtained by this formula should be multiplied by 100.

One advantage of the alpha index is that there is a good spread of index numbers ranging from 0 to 100, with higher connectivity being shown by higher numbers. All simple networks give a figure of 0, and if the index reaches 100 then every possible link must exist.

The alpha for the network shown in Fig. 95 is:

$$\frac{7-6+1}{12-5} = \frac{2}{7} \times 100 = 28\%$$

This means the network has 28% of the possible number of circuits. The alpha index for the network shown in Fig. 97 is 16%.

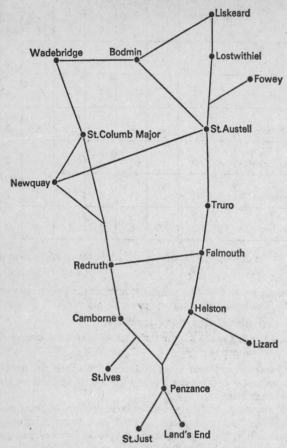

FIG. 97   *Topological map of main roads in Cornwall.*

ACCESSIBILITY

10. Shimbel. Networks are also worthy of study for accessibility as can be seen in Fig. 98. A matrix may be compiled to show the number of edges separating the different nodes. A standard technique for this particular task is called the Shimbel index. This index measures the accessibility of one node to all others, and so can be used to show the number of edges required to connect any node with all the other nodes on the network by the shortest route. By adding all the Shimbel indices together and dividing by the number of nodes, the mean Shimbel index may be discovered. In Fig. 98 this is 50 ÷ 6, which equals 8.33.

		A	B	C	D	E	F	Row total (= Shimbel Index)
Keswick	A	—	1	1	2	2	3	9
Penrith	B	1	—	2	1	3	2	9
Ambleside	C	1	2	—	1	1	2	7
Windermere	D	2	1	1	—	2	1	7
Broughton	E	2	3	1	2	—	1	9
Newby Bridge	F	3	2	2	1	1	—	9

Total 50

FIG. 98 *Accessibility matrix showing the number of edges separating the nodes in Fig. 95.*

The total accessibility of the network, that is, all the nodes related to each other, is clearly similar to the problem of connectivity. Total accessibility can be measured by the dispersion index. This may be discovered by adding all the Shimbel indices together, and in Fig. 98 is 50.

11. Efficiency of networks. Accessibility as shown by the Shimbel index is really a measure of distance, but accessibility may also be measured in terms of time. Cost comes into both these aspects, and when thinking of the efficiency of networks, it is worth considering the expression "least-cost network". Does this mean least cost to build? In which case it may be a fairly inefficient network; or does it mean least cost to the user—in which case it might be efficient but rather extravagant to construct?

12. Factors affecting accessibility. Accessibility may also be considered with reference to trunk roads, motorways, railways and even airlines. Old-fashioned forms of transport travelled directly from one settlement to the next, a system that has often been superseded; the day of the by-pass started several decades ago. Trunk roads travel from main town to main town, often completely ignoring villages. Motorways now ignore large towns.

Air routes not only ignore large towns, but often have greater problems of linking city centre to airport—as, for example, in London where Heathrow and Gatwick are up to an hour's travelling time away from the city centre.

The effect of the motorways on accessibility may be considerable in some cases. In Britain, this is especially applicable to London. Using average travelling speeds of less than 30 m.p.h. (48 km/h) in built-up areas, 40–45 m.p.h. (64–72 km/h) on rural mainroads, and 70 m.p.h. (112 km/h) on motorways as a basis, it is interesting to see how far from central London many towns are located in terms of time.

Figure 99 shows isochrones, lines denoting equal travelling time (i.e. equal accessibility, based on time). Maps can also be

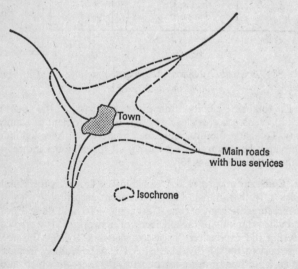

FIG. 99   *Isochrones.*

devised to show isophores, lines joining places with equal travel costs. Time taken for a journey will in some cases be a better guide for accessibility than simply a measure of distance (*see* Fig. 100).

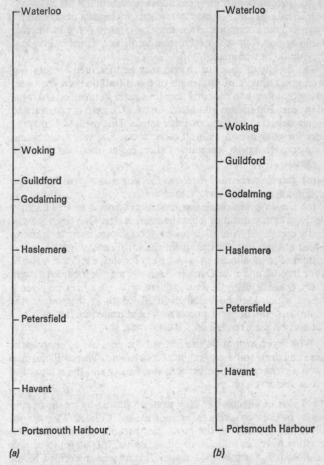

(a)   *(b)*

FIG. 100 *Topological map of the London–Portsmouth railway line.*
(*a*) Distance between main-line stations; (*b*) time-gap between main-line stations by fastest train.

OTHER FACTORS AFFECTING TRANSPORT

13. Density of communications. When studying patterns of communication it is also important to consider the density of the routes. Precise quantitative methods are essential. Scale can often be misleading here. For example, when looking at a map of South America, the communications may look fairly dense in the Sao Paulo region, but when compared with, say, Greater London, they would be well spaced.

The density of roads in an area may be measured by totalling up a good sample of the length of roads (in kilometres) and relating that figure to the total area (in square kilometres). An area of at least 100 square kilometres on an O.S. map is necessary to ensure selection of a reasonable sample. This method is precise, easy for comparison with all other areas, but very tedious and time-consuming to compile. Other easier methods may be suggested:

(*a*) *Counting the road junctions that occur in a given area,* such as a 10-km square on an O.S. map.

(*b*) *Counting the roads that radiate out from a town.* This may be done at any distance from the town centre. One town may be easily compared with other towns, though care must be taken to count at the same distance from the town centre in all cases. A system of point allocation is necessary for this, e.g. 5 for A roads, 2 for B roads and 1 for C roads. Railways may be included as well.

(*c*) *Quadrat analysis.* Each square on a map may be given a score, which may be based on road length in the square, the number of junctions, or points may be allocated on the basis of 3 for every A class road, 2 for a B class road, etc.

Whichever method is used, it will be possible to analyse the area and draw some geographical conclusions. There will normally be a close correlation between the density and the standard of economic development.

14. Index of directness. Many routes followed by roads, or railways, or even by airliners, are not the most direct. They do not cross the country as the crow flies because of relief features, existing towns or villages, or other factors. It is useful to be able to state the directness of a route. This may be quantified by the detour index, a measure of directness. It is obtained by dividing the actual distance of a route by the most direct distance (as the crow flies—also called a desire line) and multiplying the answer by 100. (This formula multiplies by 100 in order to eliminate decimal points.) If the answer is close to 100, then the route is quite efficient (*see* Fig. 101).

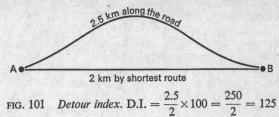

2.5 km along the road

A • —————————————————— • B

2 km by shortest route

FIG. 101 *Detour index.* D.I. $= \dfrac{2.5}{2} \times 100 = \dfrac{250}{2} = 125$

15. Friction of distance. The word "friction" is used to imply that distance is a nuisance or at least causes problems that may have to be overcome. In order to overcome these difficulties, the principle of least effort is applicable: in an efficient transport system, little effort will be involved in moving freight, or humans, over considerable distances.

The friction of distance is apparent in all forms of communication. This is true even if distance is the most direct, e.g. a fraction of distance of 1 kilometre, a cost distance of a bus fare of 10p, or a time distance of 5 minutes.

The effect of friction of distance can be seen by studying shopping visits, as the number of visits will vary inversely with distance from the market; directness of the route may be significant.

16. Gravity models. Actual measurement is essential to enable precise analytical comments to be made about movements of vehicles, people or freight. The clearest way of showing this information in a diagrammatic form is the use of flow lines. The width of the line shows how much is travelling in a certain direction. This is a gravity model, as it shows movement. The scale for the flow line may be determined by a consideration of the highest and lowest figures that are to be shown. The smallest figure will be represented by the narrowest possible line and the largest must not be ridiculously wide (*see* Fig. 102).

Gravity models are able to show flows of people or traffic or freight between towns. A relationship can be worked out between the size of flow and the size of town that will enable predictions to be made. The attractions of towns are reflected by the amount of interaction, and after predictions have been made by means of this formula, they may be tested in the field.

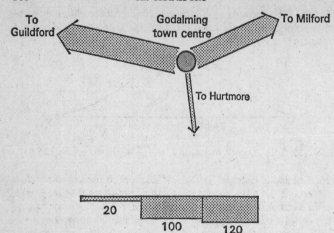

FIG. 102   *Flow-line diagram of movement of cars from Godalming town centre.*

17. Traffic surveys. Another transport study in the field involves traffic surveys. It is quite a straightforward and fruitful exercise, though prior organisation and planning is essential. A well-constructed record form is essential, and an example of this is shown in Fig. 103. The teams of field-workers are required to plot the flow of traffic past a set point, in one direction only. Each vehicle is recorded by a stroke in the appropriate column on the correct line, and every fifth stroke goes through the previous four, for ease of checking and counting at the end of the day. If traffic counts are made for ten minutes, the total flow may be multiplied by six to give an hourly rate. Graphs may then be drawn to show the flow of cars or lorries or the total flow, as is required. Traffic studies are useful indicators not only of the amount of traffic, but also of peak times, local economic development and adequacy of road networks; they are therefore an important part of development plans in any urban area.

Date _____	Name _____
Location _____	Weather conditions _____
	_____

Time in 10-minute sessions, e.g. 9.01 - 9.10	Cycles	Motor cycles	Cars	Small vans	Large vans	Lorries	Buses	
10.01-10.10	ЖH	II	ЖH ЖH ЖH ЖH III	ЖH II	I	I	IJ	
10.11-10.20	II	III	ЖH ЖH III	ЖH II	III	II	I	
10.21-10.30		IIII	ЖH ЖH I	III	II	III	III	

FIG. 103 *Traffic-survey form.*

PROGRESS TEST 11

1. What are the advantages of studying the topological version of a network? (4, II, 8)

2. Work out the beta index for the network shown in Fig. 97. (5)

3. Show and explain the variations in accessibility when measured by time or distance.   **(12)**

4. Choose five or six roads radiating from a town centre. Take each one to its first node (say, a major road junction or a town or village). Work out the index of directness for each road.   **(14)**

5. What is meant by friction of distance?   **(15)**

CHAPTER XII

Industrial and Economic Geography

INTRODUCTION

1. Quantifying industry. The success of an industry (e.g. the steel industry in Sheffield) can be easily assessed in qualitative terms using historical documentation. Indeed, historical information can be used with confidence to explain the presence of industrial activities, but as we have seen in earlier chapters, there is always a need to quantify, particularly here in a topic that deals with figures of profit and cost.

Economic analysis has become important in recent years in assessing the feasibility of industrial development in both the developed and undeveloped world. Models of development have been set up to show how a third-world country may respond to inputs of capital and activity, and cost-benefit analysis has been used to justify the building of motorways in Britain. Models will not only explain the presence of an activity but may also help to predict the future of some vast capital investment. Decisions have to be made quickly in the world of high finance and planning, whether by a firm or by a government, will rely on the accuracy of economic theory.

2. Major studies. Industrial-location theory appears most frequently in economic geography. Weber's model (*see* **5** below) is the basis of many works that attempt to explain the reasons for the siting of industries (e.g. Lindberg has shown its applicability to the paper-making industry in Sweden). Weber's model was concerned very much with transport costs. However, labour and power costs also play an important role in industrial location, and these two factors have been the subject of studies that assessed the effects of the Industrial Revolution, especially the rise and fall of core areas in the western world sited mainly on the coal-fields.

More recently, agglomeration and specialisation have been studied to explain the location of industries set up since the

Second World War. Industrial linkage in north-west London is used by Keeble to describe the reasons for the concentration of manufacturing industries there. The Edgware Road is a rather striking example, where electronic firms gather closely together in a relatively small area.

Government legislation and control feature heavily in models of location today. Industrial-development certificates, advertisements in the national newspapers and special development areas all suggest that there is now more to an explanation of the presence of firms than simply the availability, and costs of basic raw materials (land, power, labour, capital, market, transport).

Development policy and planning are vital parts of economic geography and they may be applied to either the developed world or the undeveloped world. Rostow's growth model divides development into four stages: "traditional society", "take-off phase", "drive to maturity" and "drive toward high mass-consumption"—these may be applied to many western countries. The gravity model (*see* XI, **16**) can be used to sort out problems of boundary location between regions. These as all models, provide a sound basis for academic study but may also help to plan out paths of development in the future.

3. Local-scale studies. Development is very important on a local scale as here it will affect and be influenced by the individual. Problems in locating London's third airport highlighted the power a minority group of people can have in economic planning. Similarly, the inhabitants of Bidowali village in the Punjab found the "Green Revolution" difficult to accept because their laws of inheritance did not allow land-consolidation to take place.

It is generally easier to study industrial functions and economic activity on this small or local scale. A systematic study of the distribution of a certain chain-store could be carried out, as shown by the location map of Marks and Spencer's stores in Britain (*see* VIII, **23**). A questionnaire devised to study a local industrial estate might reveal that it has a distinct sphere of influence on the labour market. It may also be possible to explain the locations of various industries in a small, local area, and any unusual locations would prove an interesting study.

4. Sources of information. There are innumerable sources of information for industrial and economic surveys. The following list gives a few of the more important ones:

(*a*) The Department of Employment's *Gazette*—monthly figures for each planning region in the U.K.

(*b*) The U.K. Government's *Standard Industrial Classification*.

(*c*) *The Journal of the Department of Trade and Industry*.

(*d*) 1971 census economic activity county leaflets, available from local planning offices.

(*e*) The second land utilisation survey, from the University of London Geography Department.

(*f*) *Kelly's Directory* and *Yellow Pages* will give local functions and locations.

(*g*) Many banks publish leaflets giving trade figures and economic information.

(*h*) *The Geographical Digest*, published annually.

(*i*) *The United Nations Year Book*.

(*j*) Embassies and trade associations, who will often supply information for individual countries and specific industries respectively.

INDUSTRIAL LOCATION

5. Weber's industrial-location theory. This theory was designed to show how industrialists might behave under ideal-world conditions when locating a manufacturing plant. The location (to be ideal) should be where the total costs of assembling raw materials and transporting products to consumers are at a minimum.

Weber, when devising this theory, paid attention to raw materials that were reduced in weight or bulk during processing. Weight-loss was critical when deciding upon the location of factories, since the entrepreneur would not be keen to transport materials to a factory that would later be discarded as waste. Raw materials that lose a high percentage of weight (e.g. wood used in pulp and paper-manufacturing) are processed in resource-orientated plants (i.e. located near the resource itself). Finished products like beer, which gain weight in the process, are market orientated, i.e. they are produced in plants close to the final market.

The following assumptions were made by Weber when devising his model:

(*a*) The land surface under consideration was an isotropic surface, where physical, cultural, political, economic and technological conditions were homogeneous.

(*b*) Raw materials and fuels were found in specific sites although sand, clay and water were found everywhere.

(*c*) Transport costs were directly proportional to distance, and they were equal to weight multiplied by distance (e.g. tonne × kilometre).

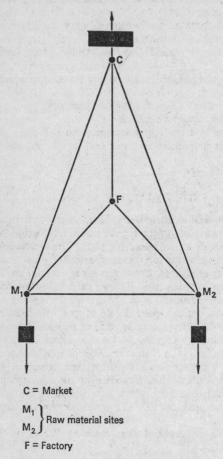

C = Market

M₁ } Raw material sites
M₂

F = Factory

= Weight or bulk of finished product or raw material

FIG. 104   *Weber's varignon frame.*

(*d*) There was one unlimited market only for each firm.

(*e*) Labour was available everywhere.

Given these assumptions, the first task was to establish a least-transport-cost location. This was originally done by employing a hardware model, the varignon frame, which employs the concept of the resolution of forces. The force of physical weights represented the influence of raw materials at specific points. Allowing it to settle, axis F is where the ideal location for the factory should occur (*see* Fig. 104).

The second method involves the geometric construction of the least-cost location based on isotims or lines joining places of equal transport costs per unit weight (*see* Fig. 105).

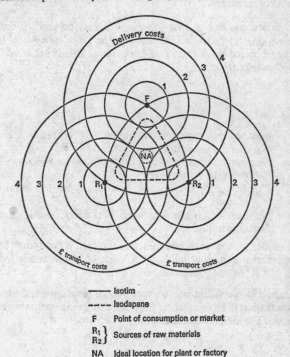

——	Isotim
– – – –	Isodapane
F	Point of consumption or market
R₁ R₂	Sources of raw materials
NA	Ideal location for plant or factory

FIG. 105 *Weber's least-cost location.*

The isodapane marks the area where least costs will be met.

This has to be modified for real-world conditions, which involve, for example, the availability of cheap labour. When taking this factor into consideration, the location of a plant would have to be such that extra costs of production arising from, say, locating the factory away from the optimum resource–market site are offset by a cheaper wage bill. The entrepreneur would have to choose a "critical isodapane" (*see* Fig. 105) on which these financial conditions are met.

Other conditions must be met, for example, agglomeration, government subsidies and other factors affecting location. They cannot easily be introduced into the model, and further study would warrant intricate statistical techniques more suited to computer programming.

6. Location quotient. A location quotient may be used to compare regional patterns of industry, e.g. the Don Valley steel industry or the cotton industry of Lancashire. This is achieved by the following formula:

$$\frac{c}{e} \div \frac{C}{E}$$

where:

c = Number of employees in industry in a specified area (e.g. Lancashire cotton industry).

e = Number of employees in all manufacturing industries in that area (e.g. Lancashire).

C = Number of people employed nationally in that industry (e.g. cotton).

E = Number of people employed nationally in all manufacturing industries.

An index greater than one indicates the region has more than its share of a particular industry. A value of less than one indicates that it has less than its share.

7. Degree of specialisation. Another way of measuring industrial concentration is by calculating the degree of specialisation within a region. The index of specialisation is calculated by using:

$$\sqrt{(P_1^2 + P_2^2 + P_3^2 \ldots P_n^2)}$$

where P_1, P_2, P_3, and so on to the last (P_n) equal the percentage of people employed, in the region of study, in industries 1, 2, 3 $\ldots n$.

The square root is the index, and the lower this value the more diversified is the industrial structure of the area. Obviously, this method is of value only when comparing indices from a selection of regions.

8. Conclusions. Locations rarely follow stringent patterns today, since industry is far more mobile than in past years, and workers and markets much more flexible. Indeed, many of the present locating sites rely more on government activity than anything else, setting up industries in the most depressed areas in an attempt to revitalise the old-core areas (e.g. coalfields).

Models designed twenty and more years ago seem to have little relevance in the present day. However, as discussed in previous chapters, models have great value in that they are formulated to give a general structure upon which past, present, and indeed future patterns can be considered.

CORRELATION

9. Paired data or variables. Correlation has been briefly discussed earlier (IV, 7): it is the mathematical expression of the association or relationship between paired data (or variables). This association can be either close or concealed, or data may prove to have no association at all. Indices produced mathematically to demonstrate these relationships are known as correlation coefficients or simply coefficients, and as already pointed out, are based on a formula devised by the statistician Pearson.

In the following examples, one of several correlation coefficients will be employed, that of Spearman's rank-correlation coefficient (r_s):

(a) When r_s equals $+1.0$, the association is perfect and positive. That is, as one variable increases, so does the other (*see* Fig. 106(*a*)).

(b) When r_s equals -1.0, the association is perfect but negative, so that the association is inverse (*see* Fig. 106(*a*)).

(c) When r_s equals 0.0, there is no association at all (*see* Fig. 106(*b*)).

However, random elements in the real world prevent perfect correlations from occurring, just as they prevent "no association at all" from occurring. As in all statistical tests, it is therefore

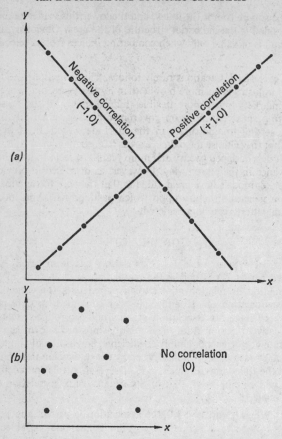

FIG. 106 *Spearman's rank-correlation coefficient.*
(*a*) Perfect negative and positive correlation; (*b*) no correlation.

necessary to calculate the probability of random elements influencing the calculation, and so it is necessary to test whether the coefficient is in fact significant.

Remember that a correlation coefficient does not imply a causal relationship, since other factors may be at play. For example, industrial production may be high in the old coalfield core areas but the reason for this may not necessarily be the abundance of a coal supply, but the injection of government capital into development areas.

10. Pearson's product-moment correlation coefficient. Standard deviation (S) is discussed at VI, **11** and these are calculated for our two variables, giving for x, S_x and for y, S_y. Since both variables may deviate from the mean value, they have a co-variance, as well as the standard deviations that each variable has irrespective of each other. The co-variance is calculated by the formula:

$$\frac{\Sigma(x-\bar{x})\ (y-\bar{y})}{N}$$

where $(x-\bar{x})$ is the measure of the deviation of an x value from its means $\bar{x}$, $(y-\bar{y})$ measures deviations of y values from mean $\bar{y}$, and N is the number of pairs of observations.

By comparing these two measures of variance in the form of a ratio we can tell how closely the two variables are associated. If co-variance and standard deviation are the same value, there is a high degree of similarity between the two sets of data. If the two measures of variance have no similarity, then correlation must be low. The ratio calculated is known as Pearson's product–moment correlation coefficient and is found by this formula:

$$r = \frac{\text{Co-variance of paired variables } x \text{ and } y}{(\text{Standard deviation of } x)\times(\text{Standard deviation of } y)}$$

$$= \frac{\Sigma(x-\bar{x})(y-\bar{y})\dfrac{1}{N}}{(S_x)(S_y)}$$

When r equals or is above $+1$ or -1 correlation is perfect but positive or negative (inverse) respectively. When r equals 0 there is no correlation.

The correlation coefficient should now be tested for significance. In the null hypothesis it is assumed that any co-variation between a pair of variables is a matter of chance association. Significance tables will either accept or reject the null hypothesis.

11. Spearman's rank-correlation coefficient. Returning to Spearman's rank-correlation coefficient, this method reduces raw data to rank values and, although some information is lost in this process, the method is quick and easy to employ, being more significant with large samples.

The data is ranked independently according to importance (*see* Table X).

TABLE X: RANKING DATA FOR SPEARMAN'S CORRELATION TEST

	1	2	3	4	5	6
Country	*Urban population*		*Industrial index* (1970)		*Difference*	
	%	*Rank*		*Rank*	(*d*)	(*d²*)
Belgium/Lux.	87	1	121	9.5	−8.5	74.25
Iceland	86	2	119	12	−10	100
Sweden	81	3	118	13	−10	100
Denmark	80	4	115	16	−12	144
Australia	79	5	116	15	−10	10
U.K.	78	6	106	20	−14	196
Netherlands	77	7	121	9.5	−2.5	6.25
U.S.A.	74	8	117	14	−6	36
Japan	72	9	124	4.5	+4.5	20.25
France	70	10	123	6.5	+3.5	12.25
Spain	61	11	153	1	+10	100
U.S.S.R.	59	12	134	2	+10	100
Finland	57	13	123	6.5	+6.5	42.25
Switzerland	55	14	111	19	−5	25
Italy	53	15	120	11	+4	16
Austria	52	16.5	125	3	+13.5	182.25
Eire	52	16.5	124	4.5	+12	144
Norway	45	18	122	8	+10	100
West Germany	38	19	113	17	+2	4
Portugal	37	20	112	18	+2	4

$$\Sigma d^2 = 14,165$$

The variables are matched pairs and a hypothesis is designed to test the significance of any relationship between the two sets of data. Null hypothesis (H_0) is that no mathematical association exists between urban population and industrial success, and that any differences are the result of random variations. H_1 is that as urban population increases so does industrial success. The rejection level is set at 0.05 (95%).

The ranks are shown in columns 2 and 4. The difference (d) between rank values for each pair is recorded and placed in column 5, and then squared (column 6). Column 6 is then summed (denoted by sigma (Σ) sign). The number of pairs is 20, which is represented by N in the formula:

$$r_s = 1 - \frac{6\Sigma d^2}{N^3 - N} = 1 - \frac{6(1416.5)}{8000 - 20}$$

$$= -0.06$$

This is the degree of association between the two variables and it can now be tested for significance. Tables designed to test the levels of significance can be found in most statistical textbooks and the extract below shows the significance value for the example:

N	Levels of significance	
	0.05	0.01
16	0.425	0.601
18	0.399	0.564
20	0.377	0.534
22	0.359	0.508

It is seen that at the 95% or 0.05 probability level, for $N = 20$, the value of r_s must be at least 0.377 to be significant.

The value of r_s in our example does not reach the critical value and hence H_0 cannot be rejected. It is necessary to examine the correlation and explain the results. The conclusions below are some thoughts on the results.

12. Conclusions. The low, negative correlation shows that urbanisation does not necessarily mean successful industrialisation. Other factors influence high urban percentages, for example, the suitability of the physical environment, as seen in Iceland. A well-balanced economy, such as that found in West Germany, does not rely too heavily upon industry, and also has a widely-distributed population.

13. Regression. When two variables are plotted on a scatter diagram it may be possible, particularly when there is a close association between the two variables, to draw a straight line through the cluster of points so that they are distributed symmetrically about the line. This can be done by eye, graphically, or mathematically, and the resulting line is known as the "best-fit" line or regression line (*see* Fig. 107). The line runs where the distances between all points and the line is at a minimum.

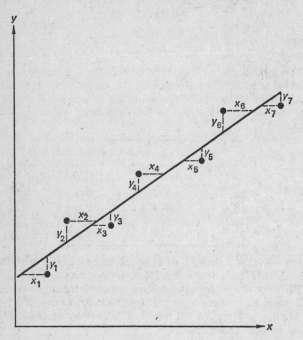

FIG. 107   *Best-fit or regression line.*

The sum of all *x* and *y* deviations should be nil for there to be perfect regression.

14. Constructing the regression line.

(*a*) *Eyeballing method.* This is inexact, but it does give a general idea of the nature of the regression.

(*b*) *Graphical method.*

  (*i*) Calculate mean values of variables *x* and *y*:

$$\bar{x} = \frac{\Sigma x}{n}$$

$$\bar{y} = \frac{\Sigma y}{n}$$

(*ii*) Read these co-ordinates on the graph to plot out point *A*.

(*iii*) Calculate mean values of *x* and *y* below point A. (Sum values of *x* lower than A and divide by number of values. Do same for *y*.) Mark this point on the graph (B).

(*iv*) Calculate mean values of *x* and *y* above point A. Mark this point on the graph (C).

(*v*) Draw in the regression line best linking A, B, C.

(*c*) *Least-squares method.* This involves a considerable amount of calculation, but is accurate. The method is designed to construct a line that, by summing the squares of the distances from the line to each point a minimum value is achieved. The mean value of x ($\bar{x}$) and y ($\bar{y}$) are calculated as are the standard deviation of x (S_x) and y (S_y).

The product-moment correlation coefficient (r) is also calculated and inserted into the formula:

$$(y-\bar{y}) = r\frac{S_y}{S_x}(x-\bar{x})$$

which will give the values of y on x.

Knowing all but values y and x, by substitution two co-ordinates y, x and y_2, x_2 can be found, providing the points through which the line must travel. Thus the line drawn is the regression line of y on x, which minimises the sum of the squares of all residuals of y.

Some x and y can never be perfectly correlated. There will be another "best-fit" line, that of x on y.

By altering the formula to:

$$(x-\bar{x}) = r\frac{S_x}{S_y}(y-\bar{y})$$

and carrying out a similar process as before, a second line is drawn.

The regression of x on y is expressed as $x = My+C$, which is the equation of a straight line. M is the gradient of the line and C the point of origin of the line where $y = 0$.

By considering the two regression lines, if they were at right angles to each other, the correlation coefficient would equal 0. When they coincide and no angle exists between them, the correlation is perfect and $= +/-1$.

15. Uses of the regression line. The regression line has three applications:

(*a*) It is a model that shows the association of two variables.

(*b*) It generates residuals that may be employed in mapping techniques.

(*c*) It allows predictions to be made, since the lines may be projected either way to estimate the unknown association between the two variables.

PROGRESS TEST 12

1. Explain the role of the model in economic planning in a developing country. **(1, 2)**

2. Show how Weber's model might be applied to the iron and steel industry. Using a specific region or country, show on the model the locations of the raw materials, the plant and the markets. **(5)**

3. Calculate the location quotient of shipbuilding in the north of England, using the following data:

	North	G.B.
Shipbuilding and marine engineering	42,000 employed	195,000
All manufacturing	459,000 employed	8,710,000

What conclusions might you gain from your results? **(6)**

4. Using *Yellow Pages*, list the types of light manufacturing in your local area. Is there a bias towards one type of activity? If so, explain why this happened. Take one particular activity and locate the distribution on an O.S. map. Can you explain the distribution? **(1–8)**

5. (*a*) Plot the values below on a scatter graph with mean annual increase in population as the independent variable.

(*b*) Calculate the regression line using the graphical method.

(*c*) How closely do the points follow the regression line?

Country	GNP per capita (£)	Mean annual increase in population % (1970–73)
Canada	1667	1.2
Switzerland	1229	1.3
New Zealand	1249	1.8
Sweden	1165	0.4
France	1046	0.9
U.K.	998	0.3
Norway	969	0.7
Venezuela	762	2.8
Austria	532	0.6
Argentina	374	1.5
Colombia	330	3.2
Malaya	298	3.7
Philippines	201	3.0
Iraq	195	3.3
Peru	140	3.2
Ghana	135	2.7
Egypt	133	2.2
Tunisia	131	2.4
Indonesia	127	2.2
Ceylon	122	2.0
Paraguay	108	3.9
India	72	2.1

(9–14)

Examination Technique

EXAMINATIONS

1. Revision. When revising for examinations, try not to work for too long in one session, or too late at night. Work in short bursts of thirty minutes or so, to ensure that good concentration is possible and that the fullest use is made of available time. Break your notes down into a shortened version containing vital words or facts. Use this condensed version for final revision.

2. Instructions. Read the instructions carefully and obey the rubric.

3. Answer the question. Read through the questions carefully, thoughtfully, and not too quickly. Only then select the questions you wish to answer. Underline the key words in these questions. In all examinations the most important requirement is to answer the question that has been set and not to answer the question you think should have been set.

4. Plan your answer. Before writing each answer, jot down a brief plan of the order in which the information and ideas will be written.

5. Presentation of the answers. Always keep the wording of the question in mind. Do not endeavour to write down all that you know about the subject mentioned in the question. Be sure to elaborate on the relevant points, whilst not wasting time on irrelevant material. Always cite suitable examples to support your arguments. Various techniques may be applicable to the problem under consideration. Think carefully about the most suitable technique for the task that has been set. Graphical work should be simple and neatly presented.

In questions about field-work, try to visualise the work involved and hence the difficulties that would be encountered. Put yourself in the shoes of the field-worker.

PRESENTATION OF PROJECTS

6. The aim of projects. To make a study on more specific subjects demands a great deal of research and enterprise on behalf of the individual. In producing an "A"-Level project it is not really sufficient to use qualitative, personal experiences to solve geographical problems. The subject-matter of many projects lacks depth, needing to be more informative and imaginative to impress an examiner, who is looking for a sound geographical approach to the piece of work. This does not imply that there is a need for complicated statistical programmes with high-powered hypotheses. Geographical techniques have their roots in clear and concise presentation, good, descriptive research and analysis with a well-argued case.

Some success can be attained by using the types of diagrams and graphs that have been discussed in other parts of the book. Most students find research an arduous and time-consuming task. However, if it is approached in the correct fashion, books and other literature can reveal a wealth of information.

All projects should aim to solve a problem or answer a question. The question may be an apparently straightforward one, but requiring field-work in order to produce the answer.

The project should aim to outline the problem or hypothesis, then to collect information that can be analysed in order to answer the question. The information should be portrayed neatly and logically—as though a small book were being written—not merely as an untidy collection of pieces of paper. Diagrams and maps should be given particular attention.

Bibliography

The following is a selected list of books and other source materials linked to each chapter. Some of these may have already been mentioned in the text.

General

A Geographer's Vademecum of Sources and Materials, G. Philip and Son, 1978.
Annual Abstract of Statistics, Central Statistical Office, yearly.
The Census (last census of the U.K., 1971), Office of Population Censuses and Surveys, St. Catherine's House, London WC2.
Facts in Focus (Central Statistical Office), Penguin, 1972.
Sourcebook of Environmental Studies, G. Philip and Son, 1975.
Statistical Yearbook, United Nations (H.M.S.O.), yearly.
Whitaker's Almanack, J. Whitaker and Sons, yearly.

Chapter 1 (introduction)

Chisholm, M., *Human Geography: Evolution or Revolution?* Penguin, 1975.
Haggett, P., *Geography: A Modern Synthesis*, Harper and Row, 1975.
Science in Geography (series), Oxford University Press, 1974.

Chapter 2 (map-work)

Fullager, A. P., and Virgo, H. E., *Map Reading and Local Studies in Colour*, English Universities Press, 1975.
Speak, P., and Carter, A. H. C., *Map Reading and Interpretation*, Longman, 1970.
Worthington, B. D. R., and Gant, R., *Techniques in Map Analysis*, Macmillan Educational, 1975.

Other sources
    Ordnance Survey, Romsey Road, Maybush, Southampton.

Chapters 3 and 4 (selection and measurement, describing and presenting material)

Harper, W. M., *Statistics*, Macdonald and Evans, 1977.

Science in Geography (series), Oxford University Press, 1974.

Tidswell, W. V., *Patterns and Processes in Human Geography*, University Tutorial Press, 1976.

Toyne, P., and Newby, P. T., *Techniques in Human Geography*, Macmillan Educational, 1971.

Chapter 5 (geomorphology)

Aspects in Geography (series), Macmillan, 1974.

Chorley, R. J. (ed.), *Water, Earth and Man: A Synthesis of Hydrology, Geomorphology and Socio-economic Geography*, Methuen, 1969.

Hanwell, J. D., and Newson, M. D., *Techniques in Physical Geography*, Macmillan Educational, 1973.

Chapter 6 (biogeography)

Odum, E. P., *Fundamentals of Ecology*, W. B. Saunders, 1971.

Pears, N., *Biogeography*, Longman, 1977.

Simmons, I. G., *Ecology of Natural Resources*, Edward Arnold, 1974.

Chapter 7 (climatology and meteorology)

Hanwell, J. D., and Newson, M. D., *Techniques of Physical Geography*, Macmillan Educational, 1973.

Other sources
   The Meteorological Office, London Road, Bracknell, Berks.

Chapter 8 (urban geography)

Everson, J. A., and Fitzgerald, B. P., *Settlement Patterns*, Longman, 1969.

Kelly's Directories of Great Britain (series).

Town Planning Review (quarterly journal).

Yellow Pages of telephone directories.

Other sources
   Estate agents and local health and housing departments.
   Rate offices of local councils.

Chapter 9 (agriculture)

A century of Agricultural Statistics in Great Britain, H.M.S.O.

Other sources

   Ministry of Agriculture, Fisheries and Food, Whitehall Place, London SW1.

   National Union of Farmers local offices for information for local studies.

Chapter 10 (population geography)

Atlas of World Population History, Penguin, 1978.

The Census, Registrar-General Quarterly Returns, Statistical Review for England and Wales Decennial Supplement, Office of Population Censuses and Surveys, periodicals.

Other sources

   Parish registers and the electoral role.

Chapter 11 (transport)

Haggett, P., and Chorley, R. J., *Network Analysis in Geography*, Edward Arnold, 1969.

Open University, *Transport and Communications* (D.291 Statistical Sources), Open University Press, 1975.

Robinson, H., *Geography of Transport*, Macdonald and Evans, 1978.

Other sources

   The Department of Transport, 2 Marsham Street, London SW1.

   British Rail, British Airways and port authorities, etc.

   Pamphlets and publications of individual transport authorities, shipping-lines, etc.

Chapter 12 (industrial and economic geography)

Davies, R. L., *Marketing Geography*, Methuen, 1976.

Wilson, T., *Industrial Location: Concepts and Techniques*, Basil Blackwell, 1977.

   There are innumerable other publications that can be of value in industrial and economic studies. Among these are the following periodicals: *Economic Activity Tables* (Office of Population Censuses and Surveys); *Employment and Productivity Gazette* (Department of Employment, monthly); *Standard Industrial*

Classification (Central Statistical Office); and the *United Nations Statistical Yearbook*.

Other sources

The Departments of Industry, Trade and Prices and Consumer Protection (Common Services), 1 Victoria Street, London SW1.

Pamphlets and publications of individual companies and organisations (as well as trade associations and chambers of commerce, etc.). Some of the national banks (such as Lloyds' *Bank of London and South America Review* and Barclays' series on countries and commodities) publish useful information. Other organisations worth approaching are the E.E.C. and the Commonwealth Development Corporation.

A Questionnaire Case-study

For a study of the shopping habits of old people in an English south-coast resort, a questionnaire was devised to assess the attraction of the main street as a shopping centre for them (*see* figure below).

Day of study	Location of survey ....
Date..	Sample number ....
Where do you live?	
Where do you buy meat, bread and sugar?	
How often do you shop at this place?	
How often do you shop in the town centre?	
What do you buy there?	
How do you travel?	
Is it easy to travel to the town centre?	
Do you prefer to shop locally or in the town centre?.......................................	
Why?	

The sampler would first have to estimate the age of the person to be sampled to ensure they were in the correct age-group. Questions then asked should be made as simple as possible and the survey itself as short as possible. In this particular survey, problems arise in that old people are poor of hearing, have a fear of surveys and sometimes lack comprehension. The form of this questionnaire (as all questionnaires) is affected by the following factors:

(*a*) The willingness of individuals to divulge personal information. What may not seem personal to you may be very personal to others. A *yes/no* answer scheme is often a way round. The sampler may also find it necessary to "lead" the person sampled round to give the appropriate answer in a conversation.

(*b*) Simple replies of a *yes/no* nature, of ticks in a box, will be easy to analyse and distinct pictures will emerge. Long-winded answers are often hazy and difficult to categorise.

(*c*) A pilot survey is necessary to test the form of the question-naire—even by asking those surveyed to suggest improvements to the questions. The pilot survey need not be large, but it should be random and as well organised as the main survey. A pilot survey will reveal information that might lead the sampler to alter his project.

Random-number Tables

61	89	04	24	98	65	96	96	77	21	09	46	81	65	05	75	47	05	29	68	12	96	68	09
33	79	53	35	51	56	11	78	52	98	48	72	35	04	54	44	95	57	83	37	03	85	01	79
96	84	68	33	84	15	08	10	83	65	30	80	15	96	05	62	00	71	13	73	72	53	19	51
28	34	05	81	54	02	60	18	77	70	76	15	92	74	05	54	09	11	90	31	22	24	17	45
19	35	37	56	39	97	66	15	58	15	53	20	57	39	58	58	70	94	52	29	53	72	70	32
37	21	22	09	18	99	33	03	78	77	72	37	07	53	88	38	54	73	75	41	40	27	69	43
46	77	77	83	19	39	43	48	28	87	28	67	76	88	69	38	52	92	65	44	67	77	01	14
12	44	97	58	79	57	42	30	33	66	37	00	69	11	52	02	43	15	58	76	16	08	85	65
08	91	47	87	38	21	74	24	98	67	00	01	19	40	03	08	69	22	52	29	57	19	05	54
98	17	54	62	62	21	06	90	27	54	16	68	45	07	19	38	88	55	28	68	50	02	39	82
73	53	29	99	11	76	30	00	94	05	91	15	28	45	32	58	29	18	50	40	14	99	09	70
35	28	06	62	12	99	48	48	18	31	34	33	59	47	23	63	48	49	10	23	91	67	32	61
50	34	68	74	61	42	19	63	19	50	19	98	51	91	18	11	65	10	88	37	41	06	93	12
95	49	75	96	49	81	93	10	37	12	92	47	03	83	48	91	32	49	19	02	91	33	55	83
22	30	86	92	56	79	71	50	35	69	47	42	42	69	31	78	72	68	76	37	59	33	22	96
68	83	63	59	30	55	37	20	44	96	85	03	67	35	58	47	79	85	74	53	00	08	03	72
69	67	64	05	14	37	16	36	13	79	91	43	62	73	11	21	93	33	56	38	88	11	02	16
04	43	66	24	01	62	72	98	91	59	55	66	49	09	52	00	85	34	72	83	48	04	90	31
03	40	89	99	66	22	11	32	91	71	47	88	38	44	75	46	55	58	32	04	86	18	00	18
95	44	09	92	08	41	49	27	89	96	89	13	41	72	11	97	96	94	41	33	85	30	57	68

Index

193

Details of other titles on related
subjects can be found on
the following pages.

For a full list of titles and prices write for the
FREE Macdonald & Evans Geography
catalogue, available from: Department BP1
Macdonald & Evans Ltd., Estover Road,
Plymouth PL6 7PZ

Economic Geography
H. ROBINSON

An invaluable work for professional students taking Economic Geography at intermediate level. Banking students, in particular, will find this HANDBOOK of value when preparing for their examinations in the subject.
Illustrated

A Geography of the British Isles
W. J. KING

This HANDBOOK presents the essential features of the geography of the British Isles in an easily digestible form. Following a logical progression from the physical environment to its human use and settlement, the author describes the resources and trends in the country, pointing the way to possible changes.
Illustrated

Geology
A. W. R. POTTER & H. ROBINSON

This HANDBOOK covers the meaning and scope of the science of geology, as well as such subjects as the rocks of the earth's crust; fossil groups; the origin, structure and composition of the earth; surface processes and weathering; and the work of ice, wind and sea. The book is amply illustrated and includes a glossary of terms.
Illustrated

Human Geography
H. ROBINSON

This HANDBOOK gives the student starting a course in human geography a basic understanding of world problems, and covers the topics commonly found in most syllabuses.
Illustrated

Physical Geography
H. ROBINSON

This HANDBOOK has been prepared to meet the needs of students taking G.C.E., R.S.A., and comparable examinations. It should also be of help to anyone who desires to have some basic knowledge of the physical environment — land, air and ocean — of the Earth upon which we live.

Illustrated

Weather and Climate
R. G. WOODCOCK

This HANDBOOK provides a concise set of study notes for students preparing for G.C.E. "O" and "A" Level and professional examinations. The material is simply stated and clearly organised. It covers weather forecasting, weather instruments, weather systems, atmospheric movement, water, temperature, microclimatology, climatology, natural vegetation and climatic types.

Illustrated